Erin King Younkins is an occupational therapist and a certified health coach. She practices therapy aimed at restoring patients to their best function through the eyes of a coach who sees the potential and possibility within each person to achieve greater holistic wellness. Driven by her belief that every human life is valuable, Erin integrates innovations in nutrigenomics and epigenetics with traditional holistic health practices to create a better model for delivering preventative and restorative wellness.

When she's not coaching clients, Erin spends her time coaching three phenomenal kids and enjoying the outdoors. She believes wholeheartedly that you were 'designed to be well.'

To Siena, Kara, and Noah—being your mom is my most favorite and most important work. You inspire me to be well.

To my parents—thank you for making each sacrifice a joyful gift. I can't thank you enough.

Erin King Younkins

DESIGNED TO BE WELL

A Health Coach's Guide to Navigating the Science and Spirituality of Wellness

AUSTIN MACAULEY PUBLISHERS™
LONDON • CAMBRIDGE • NEW YORK • SHARJAH

Ordering Information:
Quantity sales: special discounts are available on quantity purchases by corporations, associations, and others. For details, contact the publisher at the address below.

Publisher's Cataloging-in-Publication data
Younkins, Erin King
Designed to Be Well
A Health Coach's Guide to Navigating the Science and Spirituality of Wellness

ISBN 9781643784465 (Paperback)
ISBN 9781643784472 (Hardback)
ISBN 9781645367833 (ePub e-book)

Library of congress Control number: 2019906999

The main category of the book — Self-Help / Personal Growth / General

www.austinmacauley.com/us

First Published (2019)
Austin Macauley Publishers LLC
40 Wall Street, 28th Floor
New York, NY 10005
USA

mail-usa@austinmacauley.com

+1 (646) 5125767

I am so grateful for the kind words of encouragement I have received from family, friends, coworkers, and authors I admire. I feel honored to be a part of such a supportive tribe. And to Lisa Senior—thank you for taking the time to share your thoughts and support, they meant more than you know.

Thank you Paul for making this physically, mentally, and spiritually possible.

Table of Contents

Introduction

I believe we were designed. The science of our existence and evolution is fascinating, but at the heart of it all, I believe in intention over chance. I believe in an Intelligent Creator and the value of each human life. You may or may not, and that's OK; this book isn't about debating the existence of God. I am not at all qualified to write that book. This book is the why and the what of my work and my life. After years of working with patients, raising my children, and seeking meaning in my life, I needed to refocus and rediscover my talents and purpose in order to make a plan to help the people around me while I continue to learn. It is driven by my desire to see the people around me overcome their own obstacles and my certainty that wellness is possible. And it is the product of the invaluable advice and guidance that I continue to receive as I seek to understand myself and my purpose better than I did before. I do believe in God and I'll refer to my beliefs throughout these chapters, but my objective isn't to convince you of my beliefs. My goal is to show you that you were designed to be well. You were designed to live a life that matters.

I don't know you. I don't know the pain you suffer, the successes you've had, or what's waiting down the road for you. But I do believe that you have a body, mind, and soul. And I believe that you have a purpose. While the trend in our society and in our world has been to 'do what makes you happy' and 'seek your own truth,' I still believe that discovering and pursuing our purpose remains the main objective for those who want to understand the meaning of life and the meaning of their existence. Again, I am not qualified to write a book on the meaning of life, but I do want to offer to you a different way to think about yourself and how to be well as you continue on your journey.

What I want to share with you is that you have been given the body, mind, and soul you need to pursue purpose and truth. You have been designed to tread the path ahead of you and to fulfill your specific tasks in life. You are, all at once, a completely unique individual and not so different from the other unique individuals around you.

My own focused pursuit of wellness began in my early twenties. I had symptoms of psoriatic arthritis that were, at times, quite severe. It took a little time to figure out exactly what was causing my pain, and when we did, my doctor offered very little guidance and simply wrote me a prescription for a medication with intense side effects. This was not an acceptable solution and only fed my fears and anxieties which included (but were not limited to) medications and their side effects. I was fortunate to be beginning a career in rehabilitation and from the beginning of my practice, believed strongly that recovering from illness and injury was only a part of the challenge; learning how to prevent future illnesses and injuries was even more important. In addition to the arthritis and pain that I was experiencing, I was also suffering from panic attacks. I didn't like to refer to them as such and spent many years denying it and fighting the label. A pragmatist at heart, I believed that something else had to be causing my symptoms because I was neither afraid nor depressed and couldn't be suffering from something as 'silly' as panic attacks. What I later came to learn in my practice as a therapist and in my personal life was how incredibly common panic attacks are and how stress on body, mind, and soul contribute to them.

Over the years, I have had the great honor of practicing therapy and assisting patients as they recovered from illnesses and injuries, both acute and chronic. Clinically, I love being an occupational therapist for what I am able to learn and apply. I have equal access to physical modalities, cognitive interventions, and psychosocial practice. But for me, the real joy of being a therapist, and now health coach, is the opportunity to meet people. The experience of helping to rehabilitate someone is an intimate one. And while I certainly don't experience an intense connection to each and every person I work with, I do believe that each person you meet leaves a mark, whether you know it at the time or not.

I get to go to work each day, sit down, and talk to people. To truly help someone, you must listen to them first. I've worked with people from every major world religion, more countries than I remember, the very rich and the very poor, the luckiest and the most plagued, the smartest and the least abled, the most beautiful and those whom the world has overlooked. Everyone has ideas, preferences, struggles, limitations, fears, and stories. Every single person has his or her own story. I love getting to know my patients and hearing these stories. As a very young therapist, often the same age or younger as some of my patient's grandchildren, I got away with asking really personal questions and enjoyed the opportunity to listen to the wisdom of people who had already lived a lifetime.

When I was 26 and working in North Carolina, I had a lovely patient—we'll call her Marie—who was 97 years young. She was optimistic, peaceful, appreciative, and was an absolute joy to be around. She had suffered a bout of pneumonia and had an infection that made her very weak and a bit confused. Due to her symptoms, she was sent to our facility to recover while her family decided whether or not she could return home. Many of the staff where I worked believed that her confusion had not fully resolved because she was so unusually joyful and enthusiastic about life. Such qualities aren't especially common in rehab facilities—or in most 97-year-olds. I had the privilege of being her therapist and could not soak up her wisdom or demeanor fast enough. I would walk her down to the rehab room, and she'd ask to have her chair moved into the sunlight. She'd park her walker in front of her chair and stretch her legs up on to it, put her hands behind her head, close her eyes, and take a deep breath before settling in to her big familiar smile. I needed to know how to be so happy and at peace. I asked her all the questions I could think of, and she patiently answered.

Because she was so gentle and forthcoming, I took a chance on a very personal question knowing she would answer honestly. "Marie, I know your husband passed away two years ago, but I'm curious, if he was still alive, would the two of you still be intimate?"

She didn't even flinch or look the least bit embarrassed. She thought for a second and graciously answered, "If he were still alive, we would have certainly still been intimate up until last year. I don't think we'd have the energy anymore, but I'm sure we would have been until a few months ago. We never took each other for granted, we tried to take care of ourselves, and our love for each other grew every day. Physical love gets so much better when you get older because it's about so much more than how youthful and attractive you are. Young people have no idea the joys of real intimacy."

This was who I wanted to be when I grew up. Not just because she was still thinking about intimacy well into her 90s but because she was thoughtful about life. She had cared for her body, mind, and spirit and had a beautiful life to show for it.

While I may not have articulated it at the time, the relationship between physical, mental, and spiritual health was never lost on me. Those who had less pain and more ease of movement were usually happier and more patient. Those who had sharp minds, diverse experiences, and access to mentally stimulating environments were more focused, independent, and they communicated well. And while the intangibles are more difficult to describe for spiritual wellness, those who felt loved, had someone to love, and who believed in something bigger than themselves were usually more peaceful, thankful, and magnetic.

The more I learned and the more patients I treated, the more I wanted to understand wellness in a bigger way. What does it mean to 'be well'? How subjective is wellness? Can you teach someone to be well? And who is supposed to be the one doing the teaching?

Who We Are and What We Need?

Abraham Maslow is a celebrated American psychologist, famous for his pyramid describing the hierarchy of human needs. In my opinion, he gives the most basic description of the relationship of mind, body, and soul and what it means to achieve wellness. In this model, he doesn't prescribe a formula for what physical wellness is beyond the basics or detail exactly what mental health looks like but provides a fundamental picture of what humans need in order to pursue meaning.

I got my first introduction to this relatively famous pyramid in high school psychology. Simple enough to understand: humans have basic needs that must be met in order to climb the ladder to self-actualization. Biological and physical needs are the base of the pyramid, we all need air, food, water, shelter, warmth, sleep, and—according to Maslow—sex. Once we have secured these primal needs, safety is next. We need protection from elements, security, order, law, stability, and freedom from fear. This is easy enough to understand and there are varying levels of urgency. For some, the pyramid stops here because protection from the elements is not guaranteed or because living in a war-torn country makes law and order impossible. For others, the inability to progress beyond this level is due to unstable finances or health concerns. It is easy for us to see that wellness is not possible if these first two levels are not met.

Maslow's third level is about relationships. Humans seek friendships, intimacy, acceptance, affection, affiliation, and love. This varies a bit from person to person, but all people need some form of community. His fourth level is separated into two categories: esteem for oneself (dignity, achievement, mastery, and independence) and the desire for reputation or respect from others (status or prestige). The very top of the pyramid is self-actualization which is "a desire to become everything one is capable of becoming." I believe that meaningful holistic wellness can be achieved in the third and fourth levels and is required to seek truth and fulfill purpose described in the fifth level.

Other developmental psychologists and the wisdom of philosophers can further explain each of these levels. But this simplified explanation can be very useful in objectively assessing our own personal health and the health of people around us. It isn't fair to expect a hungry child to behave or excel at school. It is difficult for someone without a job or money to have a sense of wellness or to enjoy healthy fulfilling relationships. Someone who has achieved security and stability may still not have a sense of mental or spiritual wellness if they are suffering from isolation or loneliness. Service to others, creativity, work satisfaction, and personal accomplishment are all opportunities at Maslow's fourth level, but an imbalanced relationship between body, mind, and soul can create chaos and disorder that prevents a person from true self-actualization.

So why is all of this important to a therapist and health coach? Because I want you to be well. The discoveries of modern medicine are mind-blowing, but often, they are hyper focused on one part of a person. Medicine can fix a broken leg, shrink a tumor, and block all sorts of chemical reactions in the body. And all of these things are wonderful. But the 'why' is more important than the 'what.' We cannot prevent illness and be truly well unless we understand why our amazing design isn't working the way it was meant to, and I believe that harmony between mind, body, and spirit, according to God's order, is the way to resolve what ails us. I should acknowledge, at this point, that permanent disabilities exist. Dedicating yourself to achieving perfect harmony of body, mind, and spirit doesn't mean that you will never be sick. Some of the most inspiring people I have ever met battle chronic conditions or the effects of congenital disease every day of their lives. This life is far from perfect, and human nature cannot overcome all forms of disorder simply by willing it. But that doesn't change my belief that every human life is valuable and unique. Each person's journey is his or her own. Each person's value lies in the design of the Creator and not in what they are capable of.

Furthermore, the pursuit of wellness should not be abandoned because of a diagnosis. Every person has their own set of challenges ahead of them, some are visible, and some are not. Each of us was designed to be well and to fulfill a purpose regardless of our abilities.

In the chapters that follow, we will try to understand body, mind, and spirit separately and as a singular being, the way we were made. We can readily see the body. We can also see the mind and understand its existence and its role. The soul is a different matter, but for most, the belief in a soul or spirit is easy enough to accept. So here we all are, all humans, all consisting of body, mind, and soul. This concept isn't new and neither is the pursuit of self-improvement. We are inundated with self-help products that will improve our bodies, promising to make us stronger, younger, more attractive, thinner, and more able. Then there is the medical research that never rests; there is always a new drug being developed, a new disease being discovered, and a new cure being tested. And as medicine advances, so does our understanding of the mind. In 2002, a doctor I worked with at a major psychiatric hospital said to me, "Our understanding of the mind is primitive at best. We are only just beginning to understand how it works." But with each day, we have a better grasp of what it means to be depressed, anxious, or to suffer the effects of a misfiring brain. We are understanding more about learning disorders, spectrum diagnoses, and addiction. The studies of areas such as memory, happiness, and relationships are fascinating as well. And all of us want the same thing—to be physically and mentally healthy.

And then there is the soul. What it is? Who are we? Who made us? Is there life after death? Pursuit of the meaning of life and religious truth have been at the heart of the human experience throughout history. These days, there are a wide range of religions to choose from, spiritual practices and advisors to study, and access to more information than ever. The desire to understand the relationship between body, mind, and spirit has been around since man existed. Ancient civilizations worshipped their gods with physical practice, and through the ages to the present day, there are countless teachers, courses, and groups that combine physical, mental, and spiritual activities with the goal of self-improvement. But each person's journey is their own, and the battle between discovering what is true and wanting to create one's own truth is at the heart of it all.

Preparing for the Journey

As a health coach, my job is not to tell you what doctrine to believe in or what your specific purpose in life is but rather to help you achieve the condition of wellness necessary to pursue these things yourself.

Imagine you have a long road trip ahead of you. It's going to take a long time to get where you're going, in and out of several states or maybe even countries. You need to prepare for various terrain and weather. Sometimes, you'll be alone. Sometimes, you'll have to pick people up and drive them to their destinations along the way. You'll need some help from others, but sometimes, they'll do more damage than good. Sometimes, you'll have a strong satellite signal to help you, and sometimes, you won't be able to make any calls at all. There will be accidents, construction, and rush hours. You'll get hungry, sleepy, bored, irritated, excited, and confused. You'll see new things, miss old things, laugh, cry, and get lost. You might get injured and may not always feel well. You'll figure things out on your own or you won't.

And you only get to use one car. It's the only one you own. It's been driving you around town for years now without too much trouble. The engine isn't bad. The tires are OK, the brakes work, and the fluid levels are good for now. It starts up without a problem, and while it has a few scratches and a small dent, everything works just fine. The computer systems are good too. The navigation is easy to use, the radio works, and the control panel is functioning.

And you are really excited to set out on your journey to somewhere great—even if you don't know the precise spot you'll end up.

But is your car good enough for this trip? Are you sure there is enough tread left on the tires? Do you know the last time the oil was changed? Are you sure the navigation files are updated? Do you have everything you're going to need along the way? Do you even know which direction to start driving?

This is why wellness matters. You've got one body, one brain, and one soul. You cannot trade them in. But you can make improvements. And if I've learned anything over the last 17 years as a therapist, 13 years as a mom, and on my own personal road, it's this: You must embrace your whole existence. Improving body, mind, and soul together will keep you in balance and give you the very best vehicle to explore this life and serve your purpose.

So Where Do You Want to End Up?

One of my favorite perspective exercises is the well-known 'deathbed' question. On your deathbed, will it matter? What do you want people to remember about you? What will you regret doing or not doing? And it wasn't too long ago that I was able to broadly answer that question for myself, and I set out to become a coach to help people discover their answer too. I was becoming frustrated with healthcare and unsure of what I wanted to do in my career. I had been through some pretty significant changes in my life and was trying to figure out how to set myself straight and make the best decisions I could for my family and for myself. I was learning everything I could about the fascinating fields of epigenetics and nutrigenomics for my clients as well as for my family. Since food and fitness were a major part of my career, I sometimes found myself too focused on aesthetics. After some thought, I realized this: I definitely would not be lying on my deathbed wishing I had been more attractive or that I had looked better in a bathing suit. I wouldn't be wondering if enough people thought I was smart or were impressed with the things I did. I wouldn't be counting the number of races I entered or how fast I finished them. So why did wellness matter? *Because I absolutely would be lying on my deathbed with regret if I hadn't experienced the full potential of the body, mind, and soul that God gave me.* I would be lying there wondering what it would have felt like to be truly healthy. I would have wondered what it would have been like to take full advantage of a healthy, working body. I would have regretted not unlocking the full potential of a mind capable of filtering out the insignificant and pursuing the important. I would most certainly regret wasting the tools I was given because my life matters and your life matters too. The goal isn't wellness. Wellness is the condition necessary to achieve the goal. To live the life I was meant to live and fulfill my purpose, I must do what is holistically healthy and be as well as I can be.

Over the next several chapters, we'll explore the science and spirituality of who we are. At times, we'll zoom in to explore the fine details, and at other times, we'll need to zoom out to take a look at the big picture. Since I am a therapist and health coach, I'll present what I know and what I've seen help others according to the principles of assessment and goal setting. The first step to holistic wellness is knowing what your challenges are, and to do that, you need to know what to look for. Once you know how to improve your health, you can set goals for yourself. As a therapist, I have been trained to set both short-term and long-term goals for my clients, and while writing goals for the sake of insurance reimbursement is not my favorite thing to do, the effectiveness of good goal setting can't be denied. Short-term goals are the building blocks to successful long-term lifestyle changes.

These are the challenges along the way as I see them. I don't have all the solutions, but for me, it's been a good place to start. Seeking and maintaining wellness will be a lifelong task, but I hope to make the most of my life and help others to do the same. I hope to use the life that I was given to serve God to the best of my ability and to serve as many people as I can along the way.

Chapter 1
Understanding the Roles of Body, Mind, and Spirit

"You are a soul, you have a body."
– Unknown

It is difficult to acknowledge what cannot be seen, even when our understanding exceeds what we perceive. The relationship between our bodies, minds, and souls is hard to comprehend. The design of the human body is miraculous and complex but observable. The grander design of the human being, its connection to the world and to its Designer, is much more difficult to grasp. The functions of the body, the mind, and the soul are so different that it can sometimes feel easier to separate them as independent entities.

The Body

The body is the vehicle. The body keeps us alive. We breathe, eat, sleep, and walk. We see, hear, feel, taste, and smell. Our bodies demand attention with urgency while we postpone the needs of our minds and souls. And for better or worse, the speed with which we judge another person at first glance is quite literally instinctual and based on what the body looks like. The body is also responsible for connecting us to the physical. The body anchors us to the realities of the temporal world. The visceral desire for survival, comfort, and security drives our behavior each and every day. But the body is also a great gift and not something to be overcome.

I heard a beautiful homily once by Father Chuck Wible who was passionately preaching on the value of the body. He reminded the congregation that man was created in the image and likeness of God and that God then looked at what He had created and said, "It is good." Father Chuck went on to share that beyond the story of creation, the New Testament makes very intentional and profound statements about the bodily resurrection of Christ. Jesus did not rise metaphorically. His return to the disciples was not an apparition or a mere vision. He was present, fully present, in body, mind, and spirit. His body was resurrected and He tells us that we will be raised up in the same way. Yes, our bodies will die, but we will be brought to life in Christ and will have physical bodies free from disease, disability, or pain. The Bible tells us that the body is a temple of the Holy Spirit and warns us that sins committed against the flesh are particularly serious. This is not because the sins themselves are necessarily 'worse offenses' but because to sin against one's own flesh is especially damaging to one's own soul. Towards the end of this inspiring homily, he also made the connection between the value of the body and the corporal and spiritual works of mercy. Not only are we to care for our own bodies, but we have been commanded to care for the bodies, minds, and souls of the people around us.

The Mind

Though the needs and appearance of our bodies are loud and difficult to ignore, most of us would assume that our identities are more heavily rooted in our minds. What we think and what we feel can be broken up into pieces of information that we have learned and stored. Experiences shape the way we process and react. Our preferences and our abilities expressed through our choices and actions are the deeper identity that lies beneath the physical description. And the mind is powerful. Raw emotion is difficult to hide, memories can't be erased and depression and anxiety can choke the life out of our day. It works the other way too. Enthusiasm, gratitude, affirmations, and goal setting can change lives for the better. Healthy communication skills can improve relationships, innovation can solve worldwide epidemics, and strategies to cope with emotions can change the course of a person's life.

But mind body harmony is challenging to achieve, even after we acknowledge the connection. The relationship between mind and body isn't completely foreign to us, but that doesn't automatically unite them.

Mind and Body Together

Most of us have experienced the physical effects of mental stress which has prompted us to seek some improvement in our mental and physical health, but this often requires a greater commitment than what we prepare ourselves for. Let's take a closer look at the relationship of mind and body. The mind is made of the physical. While thoughts themselves are abstract, the physiology of thought is made up of cells, chemicals, and physical processes, just like the rest of our bodies. Every bit of information that we can know comes from our senses and travels to the base of the brain stem in our working memory—not to be confused with our short-term memory. This part of your brain processes (or makes sense of) the information that you see, hear, feel, smell, or taste. Then your working memory decides whether or not to store the information, as well as how to store the information. This process begins before you are born and continues throughout your lifetime, continuing to build the story of the unique individual that you are.

Your body also has autonomic functions that keep you alive. You don't need to think about how to breathe or swallow or fall into restorative sleep. And by the same process I shared with you above, your brain attempts to protect you from an overwhelming amount of data by choosing not to store information that is unnecessary. But there are also specific and conscious instructions that your mind provides to your body. Because the body is driven to eat, drink, procreate, and seek safety, judgment is crucial in coming by these needs reasonably. Freud describes this relationship as Id and Ego. The body is driven by wants and needs (Id), but the mind makes educated choices with the information available (Ego).

Thoughts and choices are only one part of the mind body relationship, though there is much more. The science of how our minds and bodies work together is fascinating. Biochemicals in the brain and body transmit messages through neurons. When these chemicals are well balanced—according to our wonderful design—we are the best version of ourselves. We feel clear, focused, and calm.

We feel hopeful, capable, and have an easier time relating to our environment and the people in it. The problem is none of us ever feels like this all the time. And many of us would report not feeling like this very often. And here is the tragic disconnect: this becomes our new normal.

Reading this, you're probably thinking, "Of course I'd like to feel clear and calm and hopeful all the time, but that's ridiculous; that's not real life." You wouldn't be wrong. Of course, no one feels like that all the time. And yes, suffering is a part of life. Days get hectic, relationships are challenging, and sickness happens. But I would challenge you to look at this from a slightly different perspective. Should you accept mediocre function of body and mind? Or were you designed to be well? Are mental and physical health available to you even though it may not be your past or current experience? Do you believe that your mind and body are capable of supporting one another and functioning in a way that allows you to pursue your purpose without being weighed down by seemingly inevitable struggles of the human condition? Later on in the book, we will take a deeper look at how your body and mind are designed to function. It's both amazingly complex and strikingly simple. Understanding the way your mind and body functions will allow you to see that illness, depression, fatigue, and pain do not need to be accepted as normal or inevitable.

The Soul

This chapter opens with a controversial quote: "You are a soul, you have a body." This quote has been incorrectly credited to CS Lewis and many scholars and philosophers take great issue with it and its apparent contradiction to some Christian values. Personally, I appreciate this sentiment and do not believe that it devalues the body at all. I believe that you can continue to have great appreciation and care for your body while acknowledging that it, in its current state, is temporary. Whether you believe in life after death or not, you cannot argue that no one lives this life forever. So, for those of us who do believe that there is life after death, it is the soul that lasts.

Again, this book is not to argue the existence of God. If you believe that you have a soul and if you believe in God, most of what follows should more or less align with your beliefs. If you do not believe, or aren't yet sure of what you believe, I hope you continue to engage in this conversation because the objective of this book is to encourage you to live well for yourself and for the people around you.

I believe in the human spirit. I believe that we were designed by a loving God who chose to create us with both intellect and free will. I believe that we were created to love, to create, to obey, and to think. I am amazed at the art and science that God expresses through life and all living things. I firmly believe that true freedom is found when we submit to the perfect design of our loving God instead of fighting against it. And because I believe in a single Creator, I believe that there is also a single truth. And the more of this truth that one can discover over a lifetime, the freer they become. Freedom to pursue that for which they were created. And just as the body provides the vehicle and the mind provides the organization, the soul fulfills the purpose. I believe wholeheartedly that a soul that is in tune with its purpose will be reflected by a healthy mind and body. Not a mind or body free from trials or all suffering, but a mind and body that are working in the way that they were designed to work.

Since the beginning of man, human beings have sought meaning and purpose and believed in a higher power. For thousands of years, priests, nuns, monks, and swamis have professed the belief that our nature is to be happy, healthy, and peaceful. Spiritual practice has involved quieting the mind, which supports a healthier body and leads to clarity for the soul. Even today, medical doctors acknowledge the positive effect of mindfulness and meditation by objective physical measures. What human beings have marveled at from ancient times up to today's most advanced medicine is this: there is a beautiful and stunningly accurate order to things. In other words, a perfect design. My children and I often watch a program on the History channel called *The Universe*. Each episode focuses on astrophysics, quantum mechanics, and origins of our universe. It is mind blowing to listen to the expert scientists featured on the show explain the math and design behind everything from the Big Bang theory to the way particles interact with one another on a subatomic scale. The science and art of it all come together in how beautifully ordered everything is. In the midst of apparent chaos, endless possibilities, and a mind-blowing scale lies the consistent and predictable math that governs it all.

And human beings are not different. We are in fact, made up of that same stardust. We are amazingly complex with an awe-inspiring order. Discovering the design that you were created according to, empowers you to overcome obstacles and achieve your purpose.

Body and Soul Together

It is easier to perceive the connection between the body and mind, or between the mind and spirit, than it is between the spirit and body. This connection is more difficult to articulate but not impossible. The body provides the outward expression of the inner state. When a spirit is at peace, the body is more relaxed. When the spirit is troubled, bitter, or afraid, the body reflects that too. The reflection goes beyond body language or facial expression. A spirit that is suffering, disconnected from its purpose and from its creator, is often reflected in real physical illness. Even modern medicine recognizes the significant effect of stress on physiology. Later in this book, we will explore the role that both mental and spiritual states can have on epigenetics and how brilliant discoveries in the way our genes work can help us to better assess the state of our spiritual health. The dichotomy between spirit and body makes it even more important to incorporate physical expression in spiritual practice and to use mindfulness to bridge the gap between the two. Some would argue that because it is what lies in the next life that matters, and because detaching from this world assists in achieving deeper spirituality, the body should matter much less, but I disagree. You were purchased at a price and your body is a temple of the Holy Spirit.

"Do you not know that your bodies are temples of the Holy Spirit, who is in you, whom you have received from God? You are not your own." (1 Corinthians 6:19)

The deep love that God expresses in His perfect design and creation of women and men, includes a stunning physical body that was made to serve, to praise, and to take part in the miraculous creation of life. To detach from the world is a valuable practice to increase in purity, clarity, and peace. But to ignore the body and its role in this life and reaching the next life is shortsighted.

Mind and Soul Together

Sometimes, the ego versus the superego. Sometimes, the head versus the heart. On a good day, they work together as an informed conscience working together to overcome the temptations of the flesh. Spirit and mind are working together all the time, but a troubled mind can often shut the spirit down and perpetuate negative beliefs, negative habits, and disordered thoughts. The mind can be so loud that it drowns out the spirit. St. Teresa used to pray that God would help her 'tame the wild horses' of her mind so that she could properly meditate during prolonged prayer. Stillness is easy enough to achieve physically, but quieting the mind takes major practice. Maintaining an even state of mind is key in remaining disciplined for physical practice and for facilitating spiritual growth. Succumbing to anger, sadness, frustration, pressure, and fatigue are regular struggles to varying degrees for all of us. A strong mental and spiritual relationship rooted in simplicity and support can foster physical health and overall balance that enable a person to pursue their purpose.

The Pillars of Spirituality

Christianity, among other world religions, recognizes prayer, fasting, and almsgiving as the three pillars of spirituality. Each of these pillars has an impact on mind, body, and spirit, as well as a dynamic effect among the three. Just as mind, body, and spirit cannot be separated when seeking holistic health, prayer, fasting, and almsgiving cannot be separated when attempting to achieve spiritual maturity.

There are many kinds of prayer: meditative mantras, scripture or other readings, free praying, or recitation of written prayer. The pillar of prayer serves the spirit by creating an open channel from us to God. Prayer is a deliberate call to be heard, it is a conversation. It incorporates praise and thanksgiving but regularly includes a petition for God's graces, mercy, and temporal assistance. Prayer can also serve to focus the mind and provide space for reflection. In a world full of noise and near constant demands on the conscious brain, prayer invites the individual to meditate and detach from the world. These days, it seems that wellness refers often to 'mindfulness' almost as a substitute for prayer. Of course, as a practitioner, it is important to not assume or impose beliefs on a client. I agree wholeheartedly with freedom of religion and understand the importance of respecting one another's beliefs. I also wholeheartedly encourage people to open themselves up to prayer, to a conversation with God, in their own way, and to view the relationship as one full of promise and potential. Mindfulness is useful as a tool to self-assess and self-regulate, and we will discuss useful mindfulness techniques in this book, but be sure not to confuse the practice of prayer with the practice of mindfulness. Prayer also has measurable benefits for the body. Since ancient times, people worship through movement and position. Modern medicine has recognized the benefits of prayer on lowering blood pressure, managing pain, and improving a whole host of ailments.

Fasting is the next pillar and its benefits are often gravely overlooked. Fasting does not just refer to food and should include abstaining from other worldly comforts, as well as abstaining from making purchases that are not crucial. Fasting provides real and tangible detachment from the world and involves the dedication and cooperation of body, mind, and spirit. The spirit leads the way by identifying one purpose of fasting.

There is a relatively well-known Bible verse that says, "Be still and know that I am God." It is a lovely, comforting verse and one that speaks to me. I wanted to dive deeper into the verse itself, and I find that one of the best ways to do that is to look at the meaning of that particular scripture in its original Latin, Hebrew, or Greek. In this case, the Latin for "Be still and know" is "*Vacate et videte*." The truest meaning of this is to be free from, or empty of, what you perceive to be real around you, and then you will truly know and be able to see what *is* real. There is nothing more real than God. Nothing is real without God.

To detach from the things of the world that chain us to what is temporary and passing is to become freer and more capable of seeing what exists outside our small experience. Fasting gives us that chance, but it isn't easy. It isn't easy, but isn't it tempting? And isn't that what the big picture is all about? Wellness is the necessary state to pursue meaning and truth. Fasting is invaluable to achieve that kind of wellness. Fasting is good for the mind too. In an age of excess and availability, fasting gives us a chance at discipline. Anything worth having is worth working for.

Achieving wellness and pursuing purpose are what it's all about, and satisfaction at the end of the road is sure to be worth it. Discipline cannot be overlooked, and there is no shortcut to growth and maturity.

The physical benefits of fasting are astounding. As a therapist and health coach, whenever I bring up fasting, there is a pretty common response that involves hesitancy and disappointment. "Ugh. I have to give up what? How many calories am I supposed to have? I can't have sugar anymore!" This resistance is usually followed up with something to the effect of: "But I have to eat every few hours, I'll get dizzy, I just don't feel right. I don't think it's good for me to fast." Sorry, that's just not true. The beauty of being designed by the Master Designer is that he has provided you with a body that can tolerate the spiritual work he requires of you. And my friends, fasting isn't supposed to be comfortable. Much like training for a race, it hurts a little. Listen to the stories of any professional athlete—none of them talks about how easy and painless their training was. But lucky for us, we were designed to be tough and to survive, and to even grow and get stronger because of our challenges.

Fasting has a phenomenal effect on the brain that is crucial in the process of cleaning out damaging chemicals and producing the protective chemicals that prevent Alzheimer's, Parkinson's, and depression. The functions that produce these chemical reactions do not turn on in the brain until it has reached a 12–15-hour duration of fasting. These aren't above and beyond measures, they are necessary! In recent years, the Paleo diet has become popular based on the narrative (and good science) that humans from Paleolithic times were healthier based on what they had access to and did not have access to. It also accounts for the fact that for most of mankind's time here on earth, there were no such things as stores, refrigerators, or constant access to food. Since the beginning of time, man was meant to not only tolerate times of fasting but to benefit from them! In addition to the brain, other organs also reap the benefits of a fast. While the body was most certainly designed to be resilient and to handle a wide variety of toxins, in today's world, we often flood our bodies with these agents faster than we can clear them out. According to the Department of Health and Human Services, humans today consume 150 pounds more sugar per year than they did 200 years ago. This has a catastrophic impact on our health and can literally change the way our genes function. How can we be surprised about the increased incidence of diabetes and heart disease?

And while we primarily refer to food when we discuss fasting, that is only one approach. Fasting can be a way to detach from many things. We can detach from money, possessions, habits, laziness, anything that prevents us from getting closer to the person we want to be or keeps us away from our Creator. Fasting from things like social media, shopping, frequent indulgent purchases, or alcohol gives our minds the space to truly assess what is going on in our lives and what changes we need to make. All too often, the excess of the world numbs us to deeper realities and stands in the way of self-improvement.

See the Big Picture

You've been walking around in the same body since you got here. You have talents and abilities, and you have challenges and pains. These days, we understand that genetics matter. We know that we are more prone to certain diseases based on what our parents and grandparents have suffered from. We begin to have small health issues here and there. Some of us ignore them, some of us are full-blown hypochondriacs, and most people fall somewhere in the middle. Our personalities and thoughts have been with us since the beginning too. You can't escape your memories, and your experiences have made you the person you are today. Our minds aren't quick to change, and we tend to have strong preferences and unavoidable gut reactions. Through it all, most people admit to sensing that there is something bigger than themselves and the world around them. It's hard not to be completely awestruck by the diversity, beauty, and perfection of nature and the universe. Whether deeply religious or casually curious, the idea of order and purpose is difficult to deny. But these are big questions!

You've got work emails to answer, kids to pick up from practice, and houses to clean. How much time do you really have to consider every aspect of your physical health, your mental well-being, and the meaning of life? Each one of us gets to answer that for his or herself. It's the first option in your very own, and very personal, choose-your-own-adventure story. Do you even want to figure it out? If you don't, there isn't much that anyone can say or do to convince you otherwise. My Sunday school students and my own children know this line all too well: "You don't have to want to be here, you have to *want* to want to be here." It's OK to be frustrated on the journey. You can be annoyed when discovered truth doesn't align with your own personal will. You can be disappointed when you have to give up certain comforts and pleasures. But you must want to know the truth, and you have to *want* to want to be the person you were designed to be. So, if you're on board for this journey, keep in mind that none of us was meant to go it alone. You'll often need help and you'll likely help more people than you realize. And all along the way, remember this: you were designed to be well.

Chapter 2

Health Coaching

How Science and the Principles of Coaching Can Help Us Thrive Spiritually

"Science and faith meet in the man who has the knowledge and knows he has been created for more."
– Unknown

Health coaching is a relatively new practice. The title itself isn't taken especially seriously in the medical community or by most consumers, but I sense that the winds are changing. In a time when immediate gratification is king and people crave quick and easy answers, the idea of having a coach to educate you, hold you accountable, and encourage you to be proactive isn't very appealing. I don't believe that this is due exclusively to laziness but that it also speaks to how exhausting it can be to juggle our relentless schedules. This is why fad diets and get rich quick schemes are so popular. People are willing to put in time and effort—but only if there are parameters. We can commit to a short-term crash diet or a temporary increase in work, but permanent changes are much harder to even consider. In this chapter, we'll talk about why health coaching and spiritual direction are worth considering, how to get yourself ready to take the first steps, and why changing your lifestyle might not be as hard as you think.

Do I Really Need a Coach?

You sure do! How's that for a quick and easy answer? Of course, that doesn't mean that you need to hire one. But here are two fundamental truths professed by many far wiser than me:

1. You don't know everything.
2. You need help.

And no one hates these truths more than me. One of my mother's favorite stories to tell about me is that my first real phrase was, "I do it by myself," and that's pretty much been my mantra ever since. You can imagine the disaster I've left in my wake. Coaching really is incredibly valuable and it comes in many forms. Look back on your own life at the most positive and influential people with whom you have been fortunate enough to cross paths in one way or another; they probably coached you. Some of the coaches in our lives are actual coaches, but some are our parents, teachers, neighbors, coworkers, or mentors who provided their guidance for just a season or perhaps even decades. Coaches can have a mighty impact on the people who heed their words, and the role is a major responsibility.

When I was a kid, I had a karate instructor who was coaching us through a performance and needed one of us to break a board. He asked a few of us to give it a try, and so I did. He didn't give me any instruction other than to 'break it.' I did my best, but it didn't break, so I looked to him for advice and he said, "Never mind. Not you, you can't do it." You. Can't. Do. It. I wasn't especially heartbroken or disappointed at the time, but I did quit soon after. At the time, I didn't think of him as a bad coach and I didn't tell my parents what he had said, but I can tell you that I believed him. When he told me I couldn't, I believed him.

In stark contrast, my children practice karate now and their head instructor has them say, "Yes, I can," at every class. All the instructors at their studio demonstrate a genuine desire for kids of all talent levels to succeed and to be the best possible version of themselves. When they hold the boards for the kids to break, they often snap them right at the point of contact so that the child believes that he or she has broken the board. This may seem like a wimpy way to encourage children, but it isn't. The instructors help them to see what they are capable of while fostering their confidence. The kids *believe* they can break the board until they actually *can* break the board. And here's the best part, all of the kids eventually figure out what the instructors are doing. It doesn't take long for them to realize that the board is being broken by the adult. And guess what? It doesn't matter. They know they are cared for; they soak up the encouragement and then get the guts up to do it themselves.

Whether we can articulate it or not, somewhere deep down, each of us knows that our successes are the result of perseverance, practice, and help. It's been said that pride is the greatest sin because, ultimately, it is the sin at the root of all others. Pride wants all the glory. Pride doesn't want help. And pride has kept so many dreams from coming true because if you can't admit that you need a coach, you'll never reap the benefits of reaching your highest potential.

The hallmark of a great coach is a true and enthusiastic desire to see other people succeed. I can tell you honestly, there are few things that make me as joyful as seeing someone achieve something they have been working on. I'm not one to cry at a Lifetime movie, but I always tear up watching the Olympics. Each of us not only needs a coach but deserves a coach who is truly invested in our success.

One of the most exciting benefits to being coached is the opportunity to learn how to become a great coach for someone else. This brings us back to wellness! Visualize the circle with me: coaches are there, along the way, to help you to understand yourself and to prepare you to perform. Coaches should always be contributing to your wellness. Whether making you physically stronger, teaching you a new skill, educating you, fine-tuning your practice, or inspiring you to something greater, a good coach should leave you healthier than you were before. When you achieve the wellness that you were intended to experience and utilize, you can do all the things that you—and only you—were made to do. I won't pretend to know all of the things that I am destined to do with my life and certainly can't know what's ahead for you, but I do know this: we are all called to be coaches. When you know, you teach. Whether it's only one person or a million; whether it's music or art or sports; whether it's philosophy or business; someone will need you to coach them. And that, my friends, is reason enough to fight through the tough times. You need to be well and be ready because someone else needs you. Coaching can only be paid forward. I can't repay my parents, my teachers, my youth ministers, or the countless people that let me learn from them, but I can pass it on.

Contemplating a Change

You don't need to be completely sold on wellness or have the perfect plan in place to begin considering your current health and what you'd like to be able to achieve. In fact, one important component of wellness and coaching is an informed and willing commitment. Half-hearted plans, unrealistic expectations, and a lack of preparation are sure to sabotage your efforts and end up discouraging you. The first step to improving your wellness is to assess your current strengths and weaknesses.

1. What illnesses or conditions am I currently suffering from?
2. What illnesses or conditions am I likely to face in the future?
3. What symptoms have I accepted as 'normal' even though they have a negative impact on me?
4. What is my typical level of stress?
5. What factors in my life contribute to feelings of sadness, anxiety, or anger?
6. What activities take up the majority of my time?
7. How often do I experience rest and relaxation?
8. How much time do I dedicate to meditation, spiritual reading, or seeking spiritual advice?
9. How often do I set time aside to care for myself?
10. How much time do I dedicate to helping others?

These questions are all relevant in an honest evaluation of who you are now and who you want to become. Building upon your strengths and addressing the weaknesses that prevent you from achieving wellness are the necessary steps to fulfilling your purpose or the self-actualization that Maslow references.

Sitting down and answering these questions is one thing, earnestly considering what you are willing to do to achieve your goals is another. Most of us have experienced the temporary desire for self-improvement. We've all started new diets or exercise regimens. We've mustered up the motivation to organize our homes and offices or develop neat and effective schedules for ourselves and our families. But life happens. And while there are certainly legitimate circumstances that derail our best intentions, more often, it is our own will to succeed that fails us. An important decision to make for yourself before you set out to achieve wellness is this: Are you going to settle for cheap thrills or are you willing to work for true happiness? There is a distinct difference between pleasure and happiness. Pleasures are the small and temporary feel-good moments in life. It isn't necessarily bad to enjoy these moments, having an ice cream cone, playing a video game, zoning out to YouTube videos, getting a massage, buying a new outfit, having a drink, etc., but they only offer pleasure in the moment or for a very limited amount of time. Once the massage is over or the ice cream is gone, there is no joy to be derived from the experience. The trouble with these small pleasures is that they produce a very real chemical reaction in the brain. These small feel-good moments produce dopamine, and your brain and body love dopamine. When your brain associates that awesome feeling from that meaningless pleasure, you start to seek out that pleasure more and more. Obviously, any of these things in excess is not a good thing. Not only do they produce negative effects over time: weight gain, addiction, irresponsible spending, or vanity, but they also prevent us from doing the things that actually make us happy.

I consider myself a runner. I run long distances and I try to train for races whenever I can. When someone who is not a runner finds this out about me, they will often say, "Ugh! I just don't get it. I hate running, I don't know why anyone likes it!" The thing that all runners know is this: no one really likes running! I love the effects of running and miss it when I don't fit it into my schedule. But even after all these years as a regular runner, I will walk around my house and try to distract myself with any other task I can find rather than head out the door and get my run started. Running hurts. The first mile is never fun. The second one isn't that great either. But my body warms up, my head clears, the fresh air starts to feel good in my lungs, and when I'm finished, I am happy. I'm proud of myself for finishing the run, I'm thankful for the healthy body I have that is capable of running and for the endorphins that are flowing. Taking care of myself produces a greater joy than YouTube videos and shopping ever could. For me, running can produce the same feel good chemicals that I would have otherwise sought out in superficial or benign activities.

Real happiness is the result of fulfilling our purpose according to our Maker's plan, and to do that, He intends for us to be well in body, mind, and spirit. Meaningless pleasures are no substitute for well-earned improvement and the chance to achieve something great. Pope Benedict XVI tells us, "The world offers you comfort, but you were not made for comfort, you were made for greatness." I couldn't agree more. The world tells us to treat ourselves and to not be so hard on ourselves, but what do we achieve by giving into our superficial desires and setting mediocre goals? Not much. Matthew Kelly has a book called *Resisting Happiness* that I highly recommend. He talks about the difference between pleasures and real joy and why the hard road is not only worth it but, often, not as bad as we think it's going to be.

Once you've considered the above questions and have come to acknowledge the cheap pleasures in your life that likely prevent you from persisting in your quest for true happiness, you need to make your way towards a decision. So now, go back to the deathbed question. Who do you want to be? When it's all said and done, what do you want people to say about you? What do you want your kids to remember? Do you want to know what your body and mind are actually capable of?

You Were Made for This

This will not be easy, but it is absolutely possible and undoubtedly worth it. And I, personally, am genuinely and enthusiastically rooting for you. Science and the passion of some very talented practitioners have led us into an age of more possibility than ever before. I mentioned earlier that I am fascinated by the field of epigenetics. Let me explain to you what this means. Your body was made to work properly. Your body was built to heal itself. Most people know that within each of your cells is a coding called DNA that holds your specific set of genes. Every person's DNA is unique (except identical twins) and is made up of about 20,000 genes. For decades, it was understood that while people have control over their lifestyle choices and habits, there is nothing that can be done about genes. This is only partially true. You cannot change your DNA, but gene expression varies based on a variety of conditions.

Epigenetics is the study of changes in organisms (us) caused by modification of gene expression rather than alteration of the genetic code itself. Basically, this means that genes can be turned off and on. You cannot change which genes are available to you, but you can foster the expression of positive genes and suppress the expression of negative ones. This blows my mind. Dr. Ben Lynch has written a book called *Dirty Genes* about seven well-studied genes and common variations of these genes that contribute to disease or, at the very least, cause unpleasant symptoms of both body and mind. This is phenomenal news for us. We live in an age when science can help us make sense of our physical and mental challenges in such a specific way that we are able to quickly identify the behaviors necessary to not only stop what ails us but to actually reverse the effects of what we have been suffering from.

As a health coach, I can help you to make a highly educated guess about which of these genes is troubling you, but you also have it available to you to discover for yourself with simple lab tests. In addition to assessing your genes, there are sophisticated labs that can test, above and beyond your typical blood work screens, for deficiencies and toxicities that you may have no idea you've been struggling with. The take-away message is this: If you have been living for a few months or a few decades with symptoms that make you feel like wellness isn't possible or that you are as well as you're going to get, don't believe it. You were designed to be well. Pain is not normal, you are not weak, and the way you've been living can get much, much better. And even if you are not interested in specialized lab testing or it is not readily available to you, you can still discover more about how you were designed to work and what your body needs to function properly.

Many of the necessary lifestyle adaptations required to change the way your cells read your genes and, therefore, function within your body are well-known healthy living recommendations. For starters, decreasing (or better yet eliminating) added sugars and increasing green leafy vegetables has a positive effect on everyone. Improving the quality and duration of sleep is also beneficial for most. And of course, one form of exercise or another is an important component to optimizing body functions. In addition to the effects that these changes have on the physical body, the mental effects are powerful as well. Unhealthy levels of biochemicals such as dopamine, epinephrine, norepinephrine, melatonin, histamine, and estrogen (among others) illicit emotions, reactions, and create habits that are difficult to overcome. Too often, the effects of these chemicals are overlooked, and unfair personality traits are assigned to someone suffering from a biological burden.

For example, imagine you are working in a high-stress office environment: tensions are high, coworkers are at odds, deadlines are looming, and resources are limited. In addition, you have a child home sick, a spouse you've been fighting with, and you haven't slept for more than five hours a night all week long. Most people would agree that this scenario would cause them some level of stress and anxiety. But for someone with an MTHFR gene variation, this scenario could be unbearable. This is because the MTHFR gene is responsible for a chemical process in the body that handles a whole host of crucial reactions including stress response. If you have a variation of this gene that inhibits your ability to convert and utilize neurotransmitters, your brain will be overloaded with chemicals that contribute to stress and anxiety which will, in turn, have physical effects.

I'll give you another example: for a child or adult with a poorly functioning COMT gene, focus and attention can be very difficult. The COMT gene plays a role in your body's ability to process major neurotransmitters, and when there is an imbalance of these chemicals in the brain, studying for an exam or maintaining order and organization is more difficult than for someone who has healthier levels of these chemicals. If you've been living with a poorly functional gene or genes (and most of us have), exacerbated by excess sugar, exposure to toxins, or incompatible medications, you may believe that the way you feel is 'normal' or that it is 'just the way you are.' Can you imagine what would change in your life if the symptoms or conditions that you've allowed to dictate your mood, actions, and choices for years was suddenly no longer a factor or, at the very least, greatly improved?

As I mentioned before, your body was built to heal itself. One of the best illustrations that I've seen to describe the way we currently view medicine, as opposed to the way we should be viewing it, was a picture of two people (in my favorite version, the people are doctors) mopping up a flooded floor while the sink behind them continues to run and overflow. If you haven't allowed yourself to discover why something is happening, you'll never be able to cure it. The best you'll be able to do is manage symptoms, which is not the same thing as wellness. And if you'll remember back to the Maslow pyramid, a life lived chasing symptoms or accepting dysfunction is unlikely to reach its full potential.

In addition to support for bodily wellness, you should seek out the expertise of those who can contribute to your mental wellness. These could be financial planners to assist you in making smart choices that contribute to your security (Maslow's second level) which can aide in alleviating stress and anxiety, career coaches who can give objective advice on business moves or skill development, or trained psychologists to help you overcome mental health issues. In recent years, the value of coaching has been studied in several settings. One of the most interesting studies I've come across was presented by Dr. Atul Gawande. In his example, he described the valuable impact that coaching had on both individual surgeons as well as whole hospital systems which led to significantly better outcomes for patients. Coaching takes the science of best practice and helps to create an achievable pathway to improvement for an individual or team.

The support for your spiritual wellness and growth should be evident in your physical and mental progress. While your coaches do not necessarily need to share all their beliefs with you, their advice should not discourage or detract from your spiritual wellbeing. Spiritual directors, religious groups, and apologists, among others, can guide you to a deeper understanding of biblical history, theology, and purpose.

These are my goals for anyone ready to take the step from contemplation to action:

1. Find a coach who has your best interests at heart, takes your holistic health seriously, and is dedicated to sticking with you for as long as you need them on your journey.
2. Take the necessary steps to discover what conditions you currently have and what you will likely struggle with in the future.
3. Assess your environment, including your physical environment, responsibilities, stressors, and relationships to determine what is harmful, what is neutral, and what is healthy.
4. Most importantly, commit yourself to seeking truth, even when it isn't what you want to hear.

Chapter 3
Wellness as a Vain Pursuit

"The result of selfishness is loneliness."
– Jennifer Fulwiler

At the beginning of this book, I stated my belief that 'wellness' is not the goal but rather the condition necessary for us to pursue our goals and fulfill our purpose. While I do absolutely believe this, I will admit, I often have a hard time not putting wellness front and center. Wellness and vanity can be very difficult to separate. When my business partner, Sue, and I set out to start our health coaching company, we had so many exciting programming ideas. We had both been therapists for years and we were eager to bring innovative and effective programming to adults diagnosed with chronic conditions. Of course, in addition to the clinical side of the company, we had to develop the business side as well. We researched companies with a similar mission as well as those who had the same target audience. The most relevant research to anyone starting their own company, whether they like it or not, is marketing. Whatever it is you are doing or making, you need to be able to sell it. Marketing research produces relatively consistent data: people buy the 'why' and not the 'what,' and people make emotional decisions more quickly and more often than they make logical decisions.

For example, there are many online fitness programs that provide workout videos, nutrition guidelines, and energetic motivation. The most successful sites are run by passionate and intelligent fitness professionals, and the information is reliable. All of this is good, and it's certainly not a bad thing if you subscribe to one of these sites. But understanding their marketing philosophy is important. These companies aren't trying to advertise health and fitness, they are selling sex and attraction. The message is that if you do what they do, you get to look like them. There are other styles of fitness that deliver different messages. Not all fitness companies sell aesthetics, hardcore strength training and endurance gyms sell competition. Let me be clear, these marketing messages do not make these companies bad. They still provide accurate fitness advice, coaching, and motivation to help people achieve their fitness goals. And I would bet that most of the trainers themselves are truly invested in helping people achieve good health. But to remain grounded in a holistic pursuit of wellness, you need to be mindful of how much you buy into the marketing message.

Body, mind, and spirit should not be separated when working towards any of your personal goals. When it comes to vanity, it is obviously the physical effects of health and wellness that tempt us to ignore our spiritual design. If you have ever lost a few pounds dieting, you'll know what I mean. People will often remark about your weight loss and about how great you look. These remarks are usually well intended and most of us don't mind hearing it. As a therapist, physical wellness was always important to me. After having children, it became even more meaningful. I had baby weight to lose in order to be the healthy and energetic mother I wanted to be, and I wanted to raise my children to be healthy as well. As the mother of three, I had as many experiences losing baby weight and 'getting back into shape,' and I remember the kind and complimentary words of family and friends when I would achieve my pre-baby weight. None of this is inherently bad and we all need positive reinforcement from time to time. But just like everything else in life, there can always be too much of a good thing.

When our physical goals aren't balanced by good mental health and meaningful spiritual growth, vanity can overcome good intentions. It is easy to become wrapped up in the new clothes you can fit into or the lingering looks of strangers. And it is at that point when the physical wellness that the body has achieved begins to hurt the soul. Personally, I struggled to incorporate spiritual fasting into my life because of vanity and, unfortunately, decided to just give up on it for many years. I would attempt to fast from food (safely and with religious intentions) but was easily derailed by the satisfaction I derived from the weight loss that followed. A few friends would make a comment or two that I was looking thinner and, suddenly, the valuable spiritual practice lost its meaning, and I found myself focused yet again on aesthetics. Eventually, thanks to a wonderful book called *The Spirituality of Fasting* by Charles M. Murphy, I rediscovered fasting and its true value. Later on, I'll share practical advice on separating dieting from fasting and how you can use this practice to foster holistic health.

While some may struggle with an aesthetic obsession, other people may be consumed by competition and winning, or find that they enjoy their success so much that they will sacrifice time, that should otherwise be devoted to family or work, just to engage in their preferred physical activities. Those who are intrinsically motivated will make their own needs and routine paramount over all else, and those who are more extrinsically motivated will seek attention and accolades from others. I have found myself fighting both temptations, and like all bad habits, admitting that there is an issue is the first step to correcting it. I am not at all discouraging anyone from setting grand fitness goals. I myself, hope to run the JFK 50 miler someday, following in my father's footsteps. In fact, I hope you do decide to set challenging goals for yourself, but I hope that they are as balanced and meaningful as they are ambitious.

And though physical goals are more obvious in their vain tendencies, mental and even spiritual goals can have similar effects. Prioritizing professional and financial success can be a form of mental vanity that leads to egocentric behaviors aimed at increasing one's own happiness and status. The excess of awards in our culture speaks to a mental vanity that we are all exposed to. Just like fitness, awards are not a bad thing, and I'm happy to watch people receive thanks and recognition for their work. But awards should never be the goal behind creativity and good works. When the drive for recognition becomes a primary motivator, mental vanity has set in.

Spiritual vanity may be an oxymoron to some, but for those who seek similar recognition or honor for their obedience and service, they will indeed be rewarded on earth for their efforts instead of heaven. "When you give alms, do not blow a trumpet before you as the hypocrites do in the streets to win the praise of others. Amen, I said to you, they have received their reward. But when you give alms, do not let your left hand know what your right is doing so that your almsgiving may be secret. And your Father who sees in secret will repay you." (Matthew 6:2)

Ultimately, one of two things will result when vanity surpasses your initial good intentions: you will either fail in your efforts because of the unbalanced dynamic between body, mind, and soul or you will succeed and your relationships will suffer for it. I quoted Jennifer Fulwiler at the beginning of this chapter from a conversation I heard on her radio show one day. She was talking about the message in our culture that, "You should do whatever you want and whatever makes you happy." In today's society, the message that it is OK to be selfish is becoming louder and louder all the time. Jennifer was pointing out how this message promises happiness, but the consequences of this philosophy in action are anything but happy. We were designed to follow the example set by Jesus to serve rather than be served, and therefore, selfish pursuits cannot produce real joy because 'the result of selfishness is loneliness.' While I am sure Jennifer wasn't the first person to have arrived at such a conclusion, the way she said it that day stuck in my head. I even started to use it with my kids. If you ask them what the side effect of selfishness is, they will immediately reply, "Loneliness." Since kids are naturally inclined to selfishness, I have used this phrase to express to them my desire to help them be the best version of themselves and that my goal for them is a full and happy life that is anything but lonely.

Wellness is very personal and can therefore accidentally become very selfish. So how do we avoid the vanity of wellness? I believe there are two main principles to overcoming the temptation of vanity. The first is to build community and the second is to commit yourself to acts of service.

Community

St. Therese of Lisieux once said, "The world is thy ship and not thy home," and my friends, we are all in the same boat! I have always loved this quote, and along with that well-known boat idiom, we can keep ourselves anchored to what really matters. St Therese was speaking, of course, about the fact that we were made for more than this world, and it is our main objective to live a life that gets us to heaven. This world is not where our comforts, rewards, or true happiness lies, and we should keep our eyes fixed on eternity with God. I love that she happened to use a 'ship' in her metaphor because the idea that we are all in the same boat can inspire us if we let it. In contrast, one of my least favorite sayings is 'to each his own,' not because I disagree with the principles of freedom and individuality, but because we have unwittingly allowed that sentiment to separate us from love of neighbor. Love of neighbor is the antidote to pride and vanity. Believing that our actions only affect us is also a consequence of the to-each-his-own attitude. Your actions, or lack of action, do affect other people. Your choice to do what you can in order to be well or your refusal to take care of yourself also effects other people. I have seen this time and time again in a rehabilitative setting. While it is surely the joyful obligation of family members to care for one another, the negligence of one member can greatly impact others and have a widespread, negative effect on relationships and opportunities for the whole family. None of us should be so careless with ourselves that we unnecessarily burden our loved ones.

Your personal pursuit of wellness should involve community in two ways. The first is to build your tribe of coaches and peers to help you along your way, as well as to identify other people that you can help to achieve similar goals. This is your *core wellness tribe.* As we discussed earlier, you will need people to help you assess your needs, structure your goals, and hold you accountable. These coaches could be professional hired coaches or other people you may know with knowledge and experience. Again, this knowledge and experience should not be limited to fitness coaches. All of us need help in at least a few mental wellness areas of our life, whether it's through counseling, work skills training, or money management. Peers are the other important piece of your core wellness tribe. Peers provide support and competition—not competition against, but competition with! We benefit from having peers to push us along the way. Isolation is a favorite weapon of the devil. When we feel alone and discouraged, it is easy to get lost in self-pity and to give up on the things we know are good for us. When you create connections in a community of coaches and peers, you help to protect yourself from discouragement and frustration that could sabotage your efforts. Community can, at times, have its downside too. There are certainly wellness communities that exude a sense of exclusivity or superiority. I encourage you to seek out generous people and organizations who challenge you to seek truth and push you to do what you are capable of doing. If you are someone inclined to leadership, consider beginning a community yourself. Starting a running or walking club, prayer group, or support group is a great way to invest yourself in wellness for the long haul.

The second way you should incorporate community in your wellness pursuit takes us back to the broader purpose of wellness. Remember the deathbed question? At the end of it all, what will you regret having done or not done? For most people, the answer to this question will, in one way or another, center on relationships. Because in the end, we know that people matter more than things. This seems obvious, but how often do we behave in a way contrary to this important truth? In the end, you will likely wish you had done a little more for someone. You may wish you would have helped more strangers, spent more quality time with loved ones, been more patient or forgiving, and all of us will likely agree that we could have been more generous. Generous with our money, our time, our talents, and our love. And this is the goal that the condition of wellness serves.

It may take time to achieve the wellness that you need in order to reach all your life's goals, but all of us can and should incorporate this work into our wellness pursuit from the start. It's good to want to lose a few pounds and to give up junk food. It's good to commit to advancing your skills or to seeking the cognitive therapy you may need to overcome mental health struggles. It's wonderful to dedicate yourself to more time in prayer and meditation. And while you're doing those things, let the great value of your hard work inspire you to always remember, that as you continue to become the person you were designed to be, you should be helping people, and can probably help many more people than you realize. I encourage you to be open to people in your life today who may be inclined to begin their own wellness journey with inspiration and support from you. That doesn't mean you'll jump into a coaching role or be responsible for their success, but stay open to helping people along the way.

As I mentioned, competition can be a good thing. The success of others should drive you to want to succeed as well. But I encourage you to remember that you are competing *with* the people around you and not against them. I am a pretty competitive person myself, but since having kids, my desire to see other people succeed has grown tremendously. I want the people around me to be healthier, smarter, and more successful. I still envy people from time to time, but my love for neighbor continues to grow as I grow in love for God. I have come to the conclusion that there is most certainly room at the top for everyone. All parents know that love multiplies, it does not get divided. I believe the same is true of success and wellness. Do not believe that someone else's success threatens your own. Bring as many people with you to the top as you can, and you won't believe how much faster you'll reach it or how much nicer it is once you get there.

Remember, we're all in the same boat.

Corporal and Spiritual Works of Mercy

'Love your neighbor as yourself,' second only to love for God, this wasn't a suggestion but an actual commandment. Even if you don't subscribe to a specific religion, 'treat others the way you want to be treated' is a popular sentiment that gets very close to the Christian commandment. If you center your wellness around the practices of corporal and spiritual works of mercy, you will be well on your way to protecting yourself against the temptations of vanity. You absolutely do not have to be a practicing Christian to incorporate these activities into your life. For the sake of sharing my own beliefs and practice, I will refer to the love of neighbor and the works of mercy in a spiritual context, but the idea of helping people who need help is a sentiment that I am happy to share with people of all creeds and all backgrounds.

The Corporal Works of Mercy:

Feed the hungry
Give drink to the thirsty
Clothe the naked
Shelter the homeless
Visit the sick
Visit the imprisoned
Bury the dead

The Spiritual Works of Mercy:

Admonish the sinner
Instruct the ignorant
Counsel the doubtful
Comfort the sorrowful
Bear wrongs patiently
Forgive all injuries
Pray for the living and the dead

We will not address each of these works in detail, but I highly encourage you to discover more about them and to consider how they fit into your life's purpose. If you're a Christian, these works are not optional! And even if you are not, I'm sure you can agree with many or maybe even all of them. Before we get into how these works are made possible by your wellness and how they can contribute to your wellness, let's revisit Maslow. While all of us may be in the same boat, not all of us are carrying the same burdens and baggage.

Imagine the climb to the top of the pyramid. Where are you on the journey? At the bottom are folks who are hungry, thirsty, and homeless. Even in the second level of the pyramid, the stress of life is overwhelming and creates a near-impossible environment for self-actualization. Because these people need to focus all their energies on bare minimal survival, the challenges of any levels above them are even harder to overcome. The corporal works of mercy encourage us to care for these people. This is striking to me because, yet again, the Bible directs us to value the body. Health and wellbeing matter, and if your fellow man is in need, you should be inclined to help.

For those higher on the pyramid, corporal works may still apply but spiritual works are more often necessary. To instruct, comfort, and forgive with love can make enormous differences in the lives of people who need help with relationships, addictions, heavy workloads, or depression. At some point, each of us needs the mercy of others through these good works, and our spiritual wellness relies on our generosity in performing them. The corporal works of mercy are a little easier to understand and to put into action. By achieving wellness of body, mind, and soul we will be more able to take care of the people around us who need it. Poverty is a timeless problem, and one that every able person should take some part in relieving. With a healthier body, a calmer and more motivated mind, and a heart increasing in mercy and generosity, the inclination to help others and the awareness of the needs of others can become a more meaningful part of your life. The best part of this? It's a beautiful cycle. As our own personal wellness fuels our desire and ability to help others, the graces and satisfaction received by participating in those corporal works serves to motivate and inspire greater levels of wellness. Volunteering and frequent acts of service have been shown to actually improve your health. Multiple studies, including several by the American Psychological Association, offer compelling evidence that not only does volunteering lead to increased feelings of happiness, but also to lower incidences of illness and greater longevity .

The last three corporal works are also physical in nature but include an even greater mental component. If you are free from sickness, pain, fatigue, and stress and inspired by scripture, prayer, and an increasing love for neighbor, works such as visiting the sick, dying, and imprisoned become more realistic and more meaningful.

The spiritual works may not immediately seem to relate to wellness, but consider this: when you aren't feeling well physically or mentally, don't you find patience, empathy, and love more difficult to come by? In order to be forgiving, patient, and concerned, it helps to be healthy. Which brings me back to the commandment of loving your neighbor. In the Gospel of Mark (12:31), Jesus tells us to "Love your neighbor *as yourself*." I truly believe that the risk of failure or of succumbing to vanity lies in this challenge: to love yourself well, because you are valuable and deserve to be well, while at the same time avoiding self-obsession. By committing yourself to works of mercy, you not only grow in love for your neighbor, but you can begin to see yourself as God sees you. You begin to see and to fulfill the purpose for which you have been made. You become a doer. The state of your wellness becomes a condition not to be celebrated with attention or admiration but to facilitate the kind life that you will be truly happy to look back on.

Chapter 4
The Unbalanced Pursuit of Body, Mind, or Spirit Progress
When Good Intentions Sabotage Holistic Wellness

"Our greatest fear in life should not be of failure but to succeed at things that don't really matter."
– Francis Chen

The unbalanced pursuit of body, mind, or spirit wellness is a struggle for all of us. The perfect harmony among each component of self is not an easy thing to achieve. Often, recognizing that there is an imbalance is the most important step in course correcting to achieve the holistic wellness we were designed to enjoy. There are two types of unbalanced pursuits as I see them: omissive and permissive. An omissive unbalance occurs when one or two components of self are neglected, sometimes unintentionally, which creates an imbalance through deficiency. A permissive imbalance occurs when one or, sometimes, two components of self are pursued too intensely, which creates tension and often sabotages good intentions.

Balance requires discipline from the body, dedication from the mind, and patience from the spirit. Let's again imagine the path ahead of you and this time, consider the luggage that you'll be taking along the way. Imagine you have a suitcase full of your physical necessities, a duffle bag full of useful books and information and a backpack with priceless mementos from your life. You are heading out on your wellness journey. Not only do you want to improve upon and add to what is in each piece of luggage but you need some of the current contents to sustain you as you go. It wouldn't make any sense to quickly drag the suitcase halfway down the road and drop it and run back for the duffle bag, to haul that a little way and then abandon that too and head back for the backpack. You may be able to travel a little faster if you only need to carry one thing at a time but, ultimately, your trip will take longer and be more frustrating. In order to not only achieve greater wellness but to enjoy the journey (yes, I said enjoy!), you need to saddle up with all three things and head down the road slow and steady.

At times, the challenges of physical wellness will outweigh your mental and spiritual pursuits. And of course, at other times, mental efforts or spiritual struggles will derail your balanced progress. As we troubleshoot the issues that interfere with our ability to balance our growth, keep another coaching principle in mind: set achievable goals. Realistic expectations are key to avoiding feelings of failure.

Unbalanced Focus on Physical Achievement

We just addressed body obsession in the context of vanity. We will continue to consider that in this chapter, but the dominance of physical wellness is not limited to aesthetics. I mentioned earlier that we are connected to our world via our senses, and because of the tangible and accessible nature of physical treatments and routines, it is easy for the focus of body goals to dominate our efforts. Running farther, weighing less, or fitting into a smaller size are all obvious measures of physical progress. Living in a competitive world where we are constantly comparing ourselves to others, both consciously and subconsciously, makes the dominant pursuit of physical wellness almost impossible to avoid at times.

Physical wellness also dominates in the world of medicine. Physical treatments are measurable, for better or worse, and the effectiveness of medicine, surgery, or therapy is observable. This makes physical treatments easier to sell not only to a consumer but to a third-party payer. This is a major factor in why wellness initiatives are not well reimbursed. If, for example, I am a doctor and you come to my office complaining of headaches and during your visit, I observe that your blood pressure is higher than normal, I can focus on that vital reading and begin to make a plan. Perhaps I'll check and see that your blood pressure has been high at each of the last three visits and then decide to prescribe you a medication for hypertension. I will be reimbursed by your insurance company for my expertise. The pharmaceutical company will also be reimbursed, and you will experience a change in status. Notice, I said 'change in status' and not necessarily improvement.

Your headaches may or may not be the result of your hypertension. You likely did not make any major changes to your lifestyle to eliminate the actual cause of the hypertension (remember that overflowing sink?), and I doubt you had much time to discuss the recent stresses in your life contributing to your physical or mental struggles. You may also have an increase in new symptoms since most medications come with at least a few side effects. However, as a patient, you will likely feel somewhat satisfied; the doctor has been paid, and the change in status proves that the treatment had at least some effect. This visit, though, does not guarantee any future health. In fact, you will likely continue to experience some sort of decline in health and will most likely require that new medication or another similar medication indefinitely, unless you decide to discover why the sink is running. This is a simple example of one specific symptom being addressed as though it has no holistic roots or holistic effects.

For those who tend to be more motivated to achieve good health, this road will be frustrating and disappointing. There may be a hyper focus on achieving physical health that feels like a constant uphill battle. Let me again take a moment to mention another issue in our current healthcare delivery system. This example is not at all intended to disparage physicians. I know several personally, work with many professionally, and have been very lucky to be efficiently and effectively treated by concerned doctors throughout my life. However, many of the struggles that doctors face these days make it difficult to engage patients the way they wish they could. Inflated costs of running a practice, managed care demands, overwhelming caseloads, and legal threats put an unfair strain on practitioners seeking to provide their patients with the best care. In addition to the challenges of the doctor-patient relationship, modern medicine tends to treat the body as something separate from the mind and soul, which contributes to our unbalanced pursuit. As a result, mental wellness suffers because the persistence of physical symptoms causes stress and frustration.

Spiritual wellness may suffer because the condition of physical wellness feels unattainable, making it even more challenging to reach higher levels of purpose or spiritual understanding. For those who are less motivated, the inability to achieve wellness becomes an excuse. The symptoms of the physical body become the justification for mental and spiritual lethargy. While it is important to maintain a solid relationship with a good doctor, over reliance on physical medication alone cannot be expected to produce holistic wellness.

Besides medicine and aesthetics, there are other ways to focus too intently on the body. Sports are a great example of this. Don't get me wrong, I love sports. As I mentioned, I love to run and swim, my children play sports, and I'm a big fan of the Olympic Games. I think sports can absolutely bring out the best in us, and I think people should try both team and individual sports at some point in their lives. However, the obsession with sports in culture has a serious dark side. In the twentieth century, children's sports grew from a handful of neighborhood boys' football, basketball, and baseball teams into a full-blown national phenomenon. Boys and girls as young as two years old can sign up to play a wide range of sports, becoming seriously competitive (and expensive!) at as young as seven years old! Again, I am a big advocate of kids playing sports, but unbalance is a dangerous thing. Instead of playing a game on the weekends and having a few practices per week, kids often have weekend-long tournaments and aggressive practice schedules that interfere with religious, family, and community obligations. Parents spend substantial amounts of money on gear, travel costs, team fees, private practices, and camps. Irrational behavior and negative attitudes from players, coaches, and especially parents are becoming more and more acceptable at games and competitions. Where is the balance in this? How can we expect our kids to learn community service, the importance of quality family time, and the value of belonging to religious communities if sports continue to dominate every hour of the weekend?

Personally, I have also experienced an unbalanced pursuit of bodily wellness when the physical goals I have set for myself were too ambitious. While the vanity of looking my best is always something to be kept in check, I also find myself committing to overly challenging physical routines for intrinsically motivated reasons. Highly restrictive diets and intense workout schedules can be very time consuming, even when aesthetics isn't the focus. It can be initially overwhelming for certain necessary physical routines to be adopted, even when they are healthy. For example, learning how to become gluten-free or sugar-free or learning how to manage diabetes can require a lot of time in the beginning. Planning meals to lose weight and to account for your workouts and activity also requires dedicated time and attention. While forming these habits has been necessary for me in the past, they have also tipped the scales towards unbalanced physical focus and caused me to lose sight of the bigger spiritual picture and neglect other mental responsibilities.

As families, and as individuals, the pursuits of maintaining our own physical health as well as the aesthetics and function of our environment can be exhausting. So, what to do when physical wellness becomes a distraction from mental and spiritual wellness or, worse yet, an obsession? The short answer is self-awareness. Just like the luggage metaphor at the beginning of this chapter, you must be willing to acknowledge that you require all three components to self and that you cannot focus on only one at a time. Your physical progress will absolutely require the intellect and organization that your mind provides as well as the will and perseverance of the spirit. To neglect mental and spiritual health is to ultimately fail your body as well.

Keep in mind these three focus questions when the pursuit of physical wellness becomes dominant:

1. Have the results of my physical wellness translated into meaningful service to others?
2. What relationships in my life have I neglected in order to pursue my physical goals, and what changes can I make to my schedule to give these relationships the time they deserve?
3. Have I maintained God, or the desire to seek truth, as my ultimate priority?

How can a coach help?

By using a health coach, at least initially, you can receive valuable guidance in setting goals that are challenging yet achievable. A health coach can also use their expertise to do the organization for you. Having a personalized plan to follow will free up time to concentrate on body, mind, and spirit balance. In addition, a good health coach should encourage you to focus on the details as you work towards improving your performance, but also help you maintain a broader, holistic perspective on wellness.

Unbalanced Focus on Mental Achievement

It is difficult to imagine what being 'too physically, mentally, or spiritually well' would look like. Remember, in this chapter, we are not discussing actual wellness, but an unbalanced pursuit of one component of wellness. Physical goals are more obvious to identify, but each of us has mental goals as well. The pursuit of knowledge or academic accomplishment is a mental goal. Financial security, career aspirations, status within a group or community, and management of relationships are also good mental goals, but an unbalanced pursuit of these goals is still something to actively avoid. Workaholism is probably one of the most obvious examples of mental unbalance.

We live in a competitive society that rewards workaholic behavior. Putting in consistent overtime results in promotions and bonuses, and taking a sick day is often punished no matter how necessary it is. The desire for financial security often fuels this unbalanced pursuit which becomes a never-ending unhealthy cycle as our definition of financial security constantly changes. If you ask most people how much money they would need to make to feel financially secure, the number would vary widely among the responses, but they would all have one thing in common: each person you ask would respond with a number that is more than what they have now. We always need a little bit more (or a lot more) to make us feel good. An unbalanced pursuit of success can lead to negative spiritual and physical consequences as we well know. When we make our own personal success paramount above all else, the condition of our most important relationships suffers, and we quickly forget our call to perform corporal and spiritual works of mercy.

Obsession with work can quickly sabotage health efforts as well. It is an age-old attitude, and one that we will address later in this book, that we will have time to focus on our wellness later. How many hardworking people are out there who skip healthy meals, skip workouts, and sacrifice hours of sleep to meet the demands of their jobs? And so, many of them 'know better.' As therapists and health coaches, we hear it all the time, "I have a lot going on at work. I know I need to lose some weight, and I'll get around to it," or "I know I need to see a specialist about my symptoms; I'm just really busy right now." Tomorrow never arrives, and health conditions continue to deteriorate. Wellness requires proactive commitment. Success requires balance. Remember, wellness is the condition, not the goal. Can you imagine how much more efficient you could be at work if you opened yourself up to the spiritual gifts that God offers you and the health that you were designed to enjoy?

The glamour of chaos is another cause of unbalanced mental focus. Our culture continues to glorify the idea that 'doing it all' is something to aim for. We are supposed to be attractive, well-dressed, well-read, charming, talented, athletic people defined by our educations and professions, driving nice eco-friendly cars, living in the right neighborhood, affiliated with the right groups of people, raising successful children who take music lessons, play club sports, get straight A's, and never look at screens. We are supposed to have nice homes that look like Pottery Barn catalogues, host book club parties, throw Pinterest birthday celebrations, and volunteer regularly at school and church functions. None of these aspirations is inherently bad, but perfection is impossible. The hyper-focused mental pursuit of accomplishments and success is a tough cycle to break out of even after you've identified it.

So how can we correct an imbalance of mental wellness pursuits? Start by answering these questions:

1. Do I work more than 40 hours per week? If so, is my pursuit of success necessary for survival, or do I choose work over spending time with the people I love?
2. Do I continue to put myself into financial or spiritual debt in order to acquire things that I don't really need?
3. Am I able to say 'no' to unnecessary obligations or excessive scheduling?
4. Have I maintained God, or the desire to seek truth, as my ultimate priority?

How can a coach help?

The right coach to help you pursue balanced mental wellness will vary depending on your particular circumstance. Career coaching via peer or expert mentoring should help you focus your efforts on meaningful goals that both advance your position as well as help you improve your services to others. A great financial planner who works to help you maximize your resources in order to be a good steward of your wealth can provide the expertise and encouragement you need to achieve discipline and apply meaning to your material possessions. And finally, a good counselor should be able to coach you towards effective communication and healthy relationships that establish boundaries and refocus your priorities.

An unbalanced pursuit of mental achievement may seem beyond the expertise of a health coach, but by keeping in mind the holistic nature of wellness, we see that health coaching can offer valuable tools to correcting this imbalance as well. Remember the exciting study of epigenetics I spoke about? You have the ability to turn some of your genes off and on. While habit changes can have a more immediate impact on your current health, when it is a matter of physical wellness dominating your efforts, correcting your unbalanced mental pursuits can play a significant role in your future healthy gene function. A qualified health coach can not only help you decode your genetic testing results to help you understand the underlying cause of your workaholic tendencies or the emotions that contribute to your outlook on life, but they can also help you to identify the conditions that you are predisposed to in your future that require your attention today. Knowing the changes that you must make today to avoid a diagnosis like dementia or other significant cognitive condition in 10, 20, or 30 years, can help you commit to a plan that improves your health both today and in your future.

Unbalanced Focus on Spiritual Achievement

The pursuit of spiritual wellness should, in fact, be dominant. As we've discussed, the importance and value of the body and mind are not to be overlooked, but the strength and health of your spirit is the most important piece of your holistic health. That does not mean, however, that there is no such thing as unbalanced pursuit of spiritual wellness. This manifests in a few different ways. In my experience working with patients and clients, there are three categories of spiritual condition that lead to an unhealthy imbalance in holistic health. These conditions are guilt, scrupulosity, and detachment.

Guilt is a difficult beast to overcome. Each of us experiences guilt on a small scale rather regularly. We may feel guilty that we ate a dessert we shouldn't have eaten, or maybe feel guilty because we bought something new that we really didn't need. And then there are more significant regrets that result in guilt that is harder to resolve. Maybe we didn't reconnect with a loved one before their death, or maybe we let someone else take the fall for something we did that resulted in painful consequences for that individual. From a secular perspective, guilt is the result of Freud's superego that assesses our moral obligation in any given situation. From a Christian perspective, guilt is our spiritual awareness that we have done something wrong—something God does not want us to do because it does not align with His perfect order. Guilt itself isn't bad if it prompts us to seek reconciliation and strengthens our resolve to do good. It does become bad when we allow it to grip us so tightly that we become anxious or despairing. One of the most powerful quotes I have ever read was from the brilliant Archbishop Fulton Sheen, who said, “Before the sin, the devil convinces us that it is of no consequence. After the sin, he convinces us that it is unforgivable.” This principle is relevant in all areas of wellness and is particularly strong when it comes to the spirit. Temptation is a powerful force. Whether we are tempted to cheat on a diet, oversleep, skip a workout, lie at work to get ahead, or commit any number of sins, humans have a knack for denial and rationalization that eventually leads to poor choices. After the deed has been done, guilt sets in and is often even more powerful than the temptation that led to the mistake in the first place. This guilt slowly, but surely, chips away at our resolve. Guilt tells us that we are failures. Guilt tells us to quit trying to be better. When our pursuit of spiritual wellness is hyperfocused on perfection, we allow our failures to have too much power over us for far too long. It is imperative to learn from our mistakes and strive for obedience and virtue, but it is also important to trust in mercy and be willing to get up each day and leave the past behind us. Evil tells us that we aren’t worth the effort, God tells us to get up and give it another try.

Scrupulosity is characterized by guilt over moral and religious issues and is objectively dysfunctional. It can become paralyzing and can have a significant impact on relationships. For someone who is spiritually scrupulous, each and every decision is picked apart to determine moral consequences, leaving no room for the mercy and wisdom of God. Scrupulosity offers little rest and makes it difficult to appreciate the little joys in life. Ultimately, it leads to stress that affects the brain and body and creates an imbalance that is very difficult to correct. Scrupulosity can sometimes impact one's acceptance of the importance of physical and mental wellness, making the imbalance worse. There are many psychiatric conditions that can also produce effects similar to spiritual scrupulosity. If our ability to make decisions, avoid absolutes, take things in stride, and relate to others with empathy and mercy is paralyzed for any reason, we will find ourselves dominated by the pursuit of unattainable spiritual goals.

Detachment is the third condition that creates a spiritual imbalance. For many people, the belief that the body has little to no value leads to countless missed opportunities to capitalize on the great gift of health. Earlier, we discussed the value in detachment through various fasting practices. Not only is fasting a great way to maintain balance, but we have bodies, minds, and souls designed to specifically benefit from fasting. However, this chapter is all about what happens when you have too much of a good thing. For those who neglect the value of a healthy body and mind and focus solely on achieving and maintaining what many call 'mountain-top experiences' through excessive detachment, the beauty and purpose of this life can be overlooked. Spiritual people will often use the term 'mountain-top experience' to describe the feelings of peace, clarity, and joy that can be achieved through meditation or prayer during a retreat. These opportunities are incredibly valuable. In the same way that a vacation away from the daily grind can renew family or romantic relationships, time away from 'the world' can provide meaningful rest and focus for the spirit. This only becomes a problem when we try to sustain these mountaintop moments indefinitely.

Detachment and fasting are important for the soul, just as running is good for the body. But just as no one is meant to run a marathon every day, we aren't made to permanently detach from the world either.

Detachment can also foster the idea that mental illness is the result of personal weakness or spiritual immaturity. Believing that we can simply 'detach' from our problems if we try hard enough is another way to sabotage our efforts. You did not create yourself; you cannot will your way to wellness. Remember that boat we're all in? We will all need a strong resolve to commit to being our best selves, but we also need help.

Start by answering these questions:

1. When I fail in my efforts, do I focus on ways to correct and improve? Or is my internal dialogue shaming and pessimistic?
2. Am I intentional in my forgiveness of others and of myself?
3. Do I avoid the pursuits of body and mind wellness believing that only the soul matters?

How can a coach help?

While prayer and the pursuit of spiritual truth and purpose are, of course, deeply personal, it is also crucial to connect with and learn from others. Priests, pastors, religious instructors, spiritual directors, and Christian/religious counselors, among others, can be incredibly useful in helping us to overcome unbalanced spiritual pursuits and providing us with insights into meaningful spiritual practice not only meant to challenge and change us, but also to bring us the peace and balance we were designed to experience. Do not be discouraged if you do not immediately find the right spiritual coach or director. Be patient and thoughtful in choosing someone to help you with this component of self.

As a therapist and health coach, I would like to point out that there will always be temporary pursuits that require more of our attention from time to time. There is nothing wrong with training for a big race, studying to pass an important exam, or taking extended time away on sabbatical. Throughout life, it will be necessary to focus our efforts more intensely on one particular component of self. This simply requires awareness. Being mindful of the imbalance created during these times in your life will help you avoid the feelings of stress or disappointment that often follow when the imbalance occurs. Of course, specific goals should have at least an estimated end date, at which point you can refocus your efforts and tend to your holistic wellness.

Have you noticed the common thread among unbalanced pursuits of physical, mental, and spiritual wellness? Self-centeredness. As you continue your journey towards the true and holistic wellness that will ultimately fuel your ability to pursue your purpose and fulfill your deathbed wishes, be sure not to fall prey to the lie that self is the most important thing. If our truest desire is to serve self above all else, we will fail. We have been designed to serve one another and it is only by pulling one another to the top of the pyramid that we can arrive there ourselves.

Chapter 5

The Unbalanced Burden on Body, Mind, or Spirit

Making Progress Despite Illness

"It's not your fault, but it is your problem."
– Aunt Gail

Coping with an unbalanced burden on body, mind, or soul is very different than correcting an unbalanced pursuit of wellness. In this chapter, we will discuss the impact of existing burdens on each component of self and discover ways to pursue wellness despite unfavorable circumstances. My mother is one of nine children, and I am very fortunate to have a big extended family full of funny, loving, and supportive aunts, uncles, and cousins. Aunt Gail is a particularly motivated and energetic soul, and one of my favorite things I've heard her say is quoted here in this chapter.

So often we waste precious days, years, and sometimes even a lifetime looking for someone or something to blame for our troubles or using our conditions as excuses. We buy into the lie that we are victims of circumstance and that wellness isn't something we could ever achieve. Comparing ourselves to others does not only fuel an unbalanced pursuit of wellness, as mentioned in the previous chapter, but it can also perpetuate misconceptions of what 'normal' and 'healthy' look like. When we perseverate on the conditions and accomplishments of others, we lose sight of the reality of our own potential. There are very real physical, mental, and spiritual challenges in this life, and it can be quite difficult to measure one man's burden compared to another. When we seek to blame externally, we can become bitter and resentful. When we instead internalize the blame, we can become self-loathing and depressed. In either case, we overlook our God-given potential to be well, to seek purpose, and to use our talents to serve. The very first step in overcoming the unfair burdens in your life is to let go of the idea of fairness. Do not undermine your own success by believing that happiness can only be found on an even playing field. Assess your deficits, accept responsibility for your future, and leave the past behind. You deserve wellness, so get out of your own way and get to work solving your problems.

Extra Burden on the Body

There are several different types of unbalanced physical burden. The most obvious is disease. Again, as I stated earlier, this pursuit of wellness does not mean that if you 'try hard enough' you will be able to heal yourself of any and all ailments. In fact, I strongly caution you against any practitioner or product that makes emphatic or exaggerated guarantees about your health and wellbeing. But improvements are always possible and are often the result of simple lifestyle commitments. As a therapist for patients of all ages, I have had the opportunity to work with some of the most severely ill and seriously injured. I have worked with people suffering from some of the most devastating congenital conditions and people who have sustained injury in more than one freak accident. Over the years, I have had the honor of working with people who demonstrate inspiring perseverance and work patiently to live and serve in spite of their physical or mental burdens.

I once had a patient with severe MS, who had only modest financial resources, outfit himself with the necessary environmental modifications, learn to strategically plan for activities, and work very hard to maintain what strength and coordination he had left in order to not only keep himself out of a nursing home, but to be able to live alone. A few years before I met that gentleman, I had a patient who lost one leg to an accident, the other to an infection and one arm to a stroke, and still she worked hard each day to navigate her world and contribute to the lives of others. I could write an entire book about the people I have watched overcome excessive physical burden (and I hope to honor them by doing so one day!) but I am sure you have witnessed a few of these scenarios in your own life. We have all met people who have overcome physical hardship that we can't imagine having to cope with. But what about your own? What about the pain that you experience each day that no one can see? What about the migraines or the colitis? Or how about the allergies that you have to be constantly vigilant about? Again, I could go on and on about the symptoms that people suffer day in and day out. When you are experiencing an excess of burden, there are two questions to ask yourself before diving any deeper into the solution:

1. How many of my symptoms or conditions are completely unavoidable? For example: blindness, amputations, congenital conditions (cerebral palsy, cystic fibrosis, etc.), or type 1 diabetes, among others.
2. How many of my symptoms or conditions are not completely outside of my control? Do I have some ability to control the severity of my symptoms or eliminate them altogether? This would include excessive weight, arthritis, headaches, food sensitivity, insomnia, heart disease, or type 2 diabetes, among others.

After you've answered these two questions, you can start to build the solution to your problem. And remember, it may not be your fault, but it is your problem, and while you will need the help of others along the way, you will also need to be an active and cooperative participant in the solution.

Disease isn't the only physical burden or obstacle to wellness. Poverty is another major factor in not only predicting wellness but in gathering the resources to overcome barriers to achieving holistic health. I won't pretend that I have experienced poverty. I have had average ups and downs in my finances, but never have I suffered food insecurity or homelessness. But to make a simple yet important point, let me share with you a personal experience of means versus scarcity. After deciding to transition to a different career focused on wellness and coaching, I made a decision to experiment with healthy but challenging lifestyle changes. I decided that for one year, I would give up all gluten and sugar and significantly reduce the amount of corn and potatoes that I ate. For the first three months of that year, I indulged in all kinds of extra healthy foods, supplements, and healthy food delivery services. Thanks to both the plan *and* the resources, I lost weight, greatly improved my health, and felt absolutely amazing. Throughout those three months, I enjoyed experimenting with all kinds of new foods and didn't feel deprived since I had access to diverse and satisfying nutrition. Unfortunately, progress with my new company and a challenging transition from my old job had put me in a financial position where it was no longer responsible (or even possible) for me to continue purchasing the food and supplements that I had been enjoying for those three months. And sure enough, even with my experience and education, I found myself back to square one and unsure of how to navigate my new financial reality in order to produce the same results. It was frustrating and depressing. On top of the disappointment, I had a relapse of the painful arthritic symptoms and insomnia that I had just managed to cure. Of course, this wasn't a complete shock to me. I was well aware, before embarking on this wellness endeavor, that healthy living wasn't cheap. But it did strengthen my empathy for those who earnestly seek wellness with few resources to achieve it. It strengthened my resolve to troubleshoot through the financial challenges of wellness and to contribute to the development of accessible programs for people who need them.

So how can you begin to address an unbalanced physical burden in order to pursue balanced wellness? I have been so inspired, over the years, by the perseverance and progress of people who suffer an excessive physical burden, either through illness or poverty, and those who find a way to thrive and to climb Maslow's pyramid, seem to have at least one thing in common: they balance the extra physical burden by strengthening their mental and spiritual wellness. In chapter four, we talked about how the unbalanced pursuit of one component of self will lead to an extra burden on the other two which will lead to a decrease in overall health. Likewise, if one component of self-suffers an unbalanced burden, the strengthening of the other two components can serve to elevate one's wellness despite the challenge.

Consider the following:

1. Take time to detach yourself from your physical illness and focus on your mental and spiritual health. Remember that you are a whole person; you are not a disease or symptom. Your physical burden is not the reason for every single issue in your life. Set aside time to assess and treat your mental health and to experience spirituality outside the scope of prayers for healing.
2. Seek to serve others. Yes, this may be counterintuitive when you are in great need yourself, but there is something incredibly powerful about lending whatever help you can to someone else and, at least temporarily, taking the focus off yourself.
3. Reassess your resources. When you are in a state of financial struggle, it can be easy to hyper focus on all that you do not have. Do not let this make you lose sight of what things you still have available to you. When you are not able to purchase more for yourself, take the time

to clean, organize, and take inventory of the things that you do have available to you. Your environment matters, take care of it as best as you can.

How can a coach help?

While hiring a private health coach may not be something accessible to all, there are wonderful resources about health, fitness, and nutrition available online and at the library. In fact, many health coaches have written books outlining their plans and recommendations that are available for you to follow. This, of course, does not fulfill all the principals of coaching because often it is the personal relationships between the coach and the individual that have the greatest impact. However, there are many online support groups for people seeking to overcome various physical burdens that can provide you with both information and peer coaching. This approach will help you to, at least, begin building your core wellness tribe. If you are able to seek the assistance of a personal coach, you will reap the benefits of a knowledgeable professional who is also 'outside the box.' By bringing a fresh approach to your situation, complete with a holistic assessment of secondary issues that you may not even be aware of, you can begin to make progress that you didn't even know was possible.

Extra Burden on the Mind

A burdened mind is a difficult thing to overcome. Some mental burdens are easier to define than others, but the ability to label them is only a small step in attempting to overcome them. In the first chapter, we examined the relationship between the different components of self and the unavoidable effects that they have on one another. Just as an *unbalanced pursuit* of wellness in one area can have a stressful impact on the other two, so too will an *unbalanced burden* placed on one component have a significant impact on the whole self. For example, it is well known that individuals with chronic or genetic conditions are more prone to depression. This is, of course, easy enough to predict. If someone is burdened with daily pain or the inability to walk, it makes sense that they would feel depressed about their condition. Spiritual burden also has a significant impact on the mind, and often, the line between spiritual and mental burden is quite blurred. Experiencing a spiritual burden will most certainly cause mental stress to some degree, and mental burden is likely to cause stress to the spirit. Though the body may not suffer immediately following spiritual or mental stress, the physical effects will eventually manifest.

We cannot list each and every mental burden, but we can consider certain categories of stress and how they impact our journey up Maslow's Pyramid. The incidence of both depression and anxiety are approximately 30% according to the CDC. That is 1 in 3 people over the age of twelve reporting signs of one or both of these conditions. There are two factors that contribute to these conditions: physiological dysfunction and circumstance. In either case, the depression and anxiety are real.

Going back to our discussion of the neurotransmitters in your brain, when you have genes that are not functioning properly, whether you were born with dysfunctional genes or your lifestyle has caused them to stop working correctly, you can experience significant symptoms of depression or anxiety. Make no mistake, this 'chemical imbalance,' as it is often referred to, does not mean that you are not actually depressed or anxious, but the solution to dealing with these symptoms is different than it would be if you were coping with circumstances that produce similar physical manifestations. There are medications that treat these conditions, and if you or a loved one finds that these prescriptions work well for you, I am not here to convince you to give them up. However, I am here to tell you that you were designed to be well, and there are important lifestyle changes that you should adopt in order to improve your health in cooperation with your medication regime. I have witnessed many arguments between those who are fiercely anti-medication and those who are big believers in pharmacology. I urge you to drop this debate and judgment of one another. Let's remember that great big ship we're all in together and continue to make better and better choices for ourselves while encouraging the people around us to also be well.

If you find yourself under a mental or physical burden too great to bear without medications, you should follow your doctor's recommendations and take what has been prescribed to you, AND you should continue to pursue a higher level of holistic wellness. Pharmacology aside, your brain does depend on balanced levels of dopamine, norepinephrine, and epinephrine to maintain a sense of mental wellbeing. Earlier, we mentioned two specific dysfunctional genes that lead to unbalanced levels of these chemicals. Methylation is the process in which the genes that control the balance of these chemicals are properly turned 'off or on.' Whether a gene is not working properly due to a genetic variation (something you were born with) or because the methylation process is compromised, the body cannot efficiently utilize nutrition to perform the function of that gene. Even though you may have been born with a dysfunctional gene, you can improve its function through the elimination of certain environmental exposures and increased nutrition through targeted meal planning. By making these changes, you may not be able to facilitate perfect gene function, but you can greatly improve the methylation process which will lead to a significant change in the balance of chemicals in the brain and in overall mood.

One very common genetic variation that illustrates this point is a dysfunctional MTHFR (Methylene-tetrahydrofolate reductase) gene. Whether you have been born with a gene variation that causes dysfunction in this gene or your lifestyle has led to its poor function, you will suffer the effects of poor methylation. One very common symptom of this is depression. Unfortunately, most people suffering from a dysfunctional MTHFR gene are often unwittingly making their gene dirtier each day by eating foods with folic acid or by taking birth control. Neither of these substances is natural and neither is meant to be in your body. This is a prime example of how the acceptance of poor practice in our current culture in both nutrition and medicine are making people sick, while simple lifestyle changes could, instead, make them well. This is the overflowing sink. Again, let me emphasize that this does not mean that a person with a MTHFR gene variation can force themselves to be well and not need medications. But if you can focus on turning off the sink, which is to say, addressing the true problem and realigning yourself with the way that God designed you to function, you will be able to advance your overall health and save yourself the trouble of either unnecessary medications or higher doses of necessary medications.

Another example of an unbalanced mental burden could stem from unhealthy relationships. Living with, working with, and communicating with the people around us can sometimes be a challenge, but truly unhealthy relationships are a different matter and can place an immense burden on the mind. An abusive, addicted, manipulative, or angry person in your life can cause a great deal of hardship and have far reaching effects on your mental, physical, and spiritual wellbeing. Abuse is of particular concern, and if you are a victim of any type of abuse, whether it is mental, physical, emotional, sexual, or financial, your wellness is greatly threatened, and you should seek help immediately. There are many resources for people who find themselves in unhealthy relationships, and before seeking out coaches who can help you achieve great mental wellness, you will need professionals and loved ones who can help you overcome this burden and address your mental health needs.

Significant threats to your basic needs are another example of mental burden. Remembering the Maslow Pyramid, when life's necessities are not secured, there are obvious physical consequences, but the mental consequences can be equally intense, especially if you are a provider for other people in your life. Job instability, financial loss, and a lack of resources for nutrition and health carry with them deep mental burdens. Poverty leads to obvious physical burdens, but the mental burdens may be even harder to bear. Poverty is dehumanizing. Each of us is far more likely to achieve physical wellness when we can afford healthy foods, have access to fitness activities, and sleep soundly in safe homes. But our mental wellness also requires adequate funding and resources to maintain stability and motivation.

So where to start when you decide to take control of a mental burden that may not be your fault but is most certainly your problem?

1. Be open-minded. Coping with an especially heavy mental burden can often cause one to feel isolated and alone. When you begin to believe everything you think, you cut yourself off from possible solutions. Begin by acknowledging that improvement is possible.
2. Sort out physical causes from circumstantial causes. While both need to be addressed, treating the physical causes first can lead to more efficient treatment of other factors.
3. Seek immediate help for mental burdens that threaten your safety and security.

How can a coach help?

Once you have achieved safety and stability, coaching can help you identify the necessary lifestyle changes you need to avoid finding yourself in the same unstable circumstances in the future. A health coach can be especially helpful in giving you the necessary support to troubleshoot through issues with new eating habits, fitness goals, and environmental changes as well, using stress and pain management techniques. Professional counselors can facilitate healthier communication within your relationships by coaching you through therapy sessions with the people in your life, and addiction sponsors can also provide crucial coaching and support to those who need to unburden themselves of the effects from substance abuse.

Extra Burden on the Spirit

Burden on the spirit is something we are all likely to face at some point in our lives. For some, this burden is unbalanced for much longer than others. Despair, loneliness, and fear are all burdens which can cause spiritual stress. These can be paralyzing to the soul and will inevitably cause illness to both body and mind.

A tangible example of extra spiritual burden would be the death of a loved one, especially of a child. Grief is, far and away, more powerful than physical or mental burden. This is not to discount the spiritual burden of intense trauma or abuse or any other pain that you may have experienced. While these may be considered physical or mental in nature, there is most certainly a serious impact on the soul. There are, of course, mental components to grief, but it is the spirit that suffers most severely. Grief changes over time, but loss is not something that can be undone. As it is the only truly permanent thing we know is death. I have worked with many clients over the years who have experienced the loss of one or more children, and each time, I'm left more or less speechless. I am, myself, a mother and cannot begin to fathom the experience of losing a child. The death of parents, grandparents, and friends can also be extremely tough to bear, especially when the death itself was traumatic or unexpected.

I would argue that tasking people with being the primary caregiver to a loved one can also put extra burden on the spirit. We are designed to give of ourselves. We are designed to be mothers and fathers, either literally or spiritually. We are designed to take care of our aging parents and other relatives as well. However, there is an extra burden on those tasked with caring for disabled children, spouses, or parents. There is an abrupt, and in some cases permanent, change to lifestyle and lifelong goals and expectations when a situation arises in which you find yourself taking on the role of permanent caregiver. There is the sadness and frustration of watching your child suffer inexplicably, a parent losing his or her memory and independence, or the person you married becoming unrecognizable because of illness or injury. In addition to that, sadness is the frustration of losing your own freedom in many ways, dealing with compromised finances while struggling to support a family and coping with the physical and mental demands of full-time caretaking. Responsibilities that were once shared may now be solely on your shoulders. The ability to care for yourself and maintain your own wellness becomes a priority so far removed that it is impossible to fit it into your day.

There are many other spiritual burdens that people face. Any particularly intense inclination towards sin can be a burden carried throughout a lifetime. Painful confusion over one's identity is another example of extra spiritual stress. And for others, like St. Theresa of Calcutta, an endless spiritual desert devoid of joy, despite immense faith, can fuel years of depression.

I heard a brilliant homily a few years ago about the fall of Lucifer, the angel turned devil. It was an incredibly thought-provoking reflection on the nature of evil and how it remains consistent with the mission of evil today. Angels are believed to have existed before humans. Intelligent beings with free will, joyously existing with God in endless praise. And then God created humans. And humans were created different from the angels. Humans were designed in God's image, and it was good. They were designed with intellect and free will, just as the angels were, but were also gifted with the ability to participate in the creation of life. Men and women were designed to bring life into the world, and we were designed to be well. We were designed to thrive in our environment, use our brains and bodies for meaningful work, and have fulfilling relationships. According to the revelation of Lucifer's downfall, he was filled with jealousy and rage over the favoritism towards human beings. God loved Adam and Eve and they were given dominion over creation. And they could create life in union with God's will. Lucifer's outrage led him to leave the presence of God and be chained to his hatred for eternity. We have all heard the story of Adam and Eve and Satan's persuasion to eat the apple. Remember, angels were gifted with intellect, and Satan is no fool. He knew that the human condition includes pride that requires obedience to overcome. But when it is not overcome and is instead placed at the center of thought and intentions, God's perfect design becomes distorted into chaos. This is why sin, above all other spiritual burden, has the most devastating impact on humankind. Our souls were designed to magnify the Lord and to live in close relationship with Him. Sin separates us from Him, the one who designed us, leaving us broken and in desperate need of grace. Holistically speaking, that which is not good for your spirit is most certainly not good for your mind or body.

While grief, loss, and trauma are concrete events that produce an inescapable spiritual burden, other burdens that we face are often the result of our own internal struggles with will and pride. But no matter the origin of the spiritual burden, everyone deserves to experience forgiveness, love, compassion, and patience that help to lighten the load.

I have many favorite scripture passages, but one in particular is about sharing burden: *"A few days later, when Jesus again entered Capernaum, the people heard that he had come there. They gathered in such large numbers that there was no room left, not even outside the door, and he preached the word to them. Some men came, bringing to him a paralyzed man, carried by four of them. Since they could not get him to Jesus because of the crowd, they made an opening in the roof above Jesus by digging through it and then lowered the mat the man was lying on. When Jesus saw their faith, he said to the paralyzed man, 'Son, your sins are forgiven.'"* (Mark 2:1–5) The gospel goes on to tell of how the Pharisees accused him of blasphemy as only God can forgive sins. In order to demonstrate to them that he did have authority to forgive sins, which he called a much greater task than that which physical healing requires, he also healed the man who immediately stood up, took his mat, and went home. When I was younger, I listened to this passage as an example of Jesus's healing power and for the interaction between him and the teachers of the law. It wasn't until a few years ago that I considered what it meant to be one of the man's friends.

I, myself, have never experienced devastating loss. My parents are living, and my children are healthy. I have certainly weathered some storms, but none that has left me bereaved. As most people do, I now have friends and family in my life who have suffered traumatic events and loss. I have watched it rob them of their peace and joy and health. And I have listened to other people judge them for not bouncing back to the person they were before the loss occurred. It has brought me to the realization that there are burdens in life so heavy that the only thing a person suffering from one can do is to survive. Just day-by-day, one foot in front of the other. The burden is so heavy that just getting from hour to hour is a job unto itself. This goes for immense pain through physical sickness, severe mental illness, or intense spiritual grief. And for those who suffer these burdens, we are called to invite them to lie down on a mat and, as a team, grab a corner and share the load. Whether anger, depression, fear, despair, frustration, or pain, we carry the weight for them since we cannot carry the burden for them. I love the visual of this passage, four friends or family members simply walking in unison, each carrying a corner of the mat, eyes looking straight ahead. As the passage is written, there are even more friends and family accompanying those carrying the mat, and I imagine their silent petitions strengthened by their physical commitment to seek real help for the burdened man. Because sometimes, that's all you can do. There is no more advice or encouragement to be offered, no more wisdom to be shared. Just to walk together towards the source of all healing, peace, and joy—Jesus. And they dig their way through a roof, and I imagine with great effort, lower their friend to the only One who can truly heal. I include this meditation here for you because if you yourself are carrying a burden so heavy that it is all you can do, know that you deserve the love and friendship of people who can help get you to a source of healing. And if you are fortunate enough to not experience such a burden, look for ways to grab a corner of someone else's mat, someone who needs your strength and compassion to persevere. The passage does not say that the man was cured because the people around him judged him or offered him incessant advice. The man was healed because his friends loved him enough to carry him through his illness.

"Greater love has no one than this: to lay down one's life for one's friends." (John 15:13)

The martyrs and heroes throughout history who have sacrificed their very lives out of love for others serve as tremendous witnesses. Most of us won't ever be faced with that kind of decision, whether to literally lay our lives down in order to save someone else's. But I challenge you to meditate on the greater picture of daily self-sacrifice. We are all called to sacrifice some comfort, some time, some freedom—sometimes at a great price—to save someone else. In the case of spiritual burden, your sacrifice could save a life or even save a soul.

Your spiritual wellness matters, and anyone suffering extra spiritual burden requires the love and support of others. If you find yourself struggling to cope with any type of spiritual burden, consider the following:

1. You are absolutely not alone. There is help for you. Remind yourself of this every day and reach out to family, neighbors, faith communities, or supportive organizations to begin building a network of support.
2. People need you. Your experience will help others. Remember that the lessons learned as you navigate your own burden are not for you alone. Do not give up.
3. Neglecting your physical and mental needs will magnify your spiritual struggle. While extra spiritual burden will make it very difficult to stick to ambitious physical and mental wellness goals, you can choose just one healthy habit, each day or each week, to focus on.

How can a coach help?

Coping with an extra spiritual burden requires a significant amount of energy and effort, and it often leaves us feeling alone. My grandfather wrote a short book called *Deus Meus*, and in it, there is one entire page which says just this: "*The Honor of Accepting: To give is wonderful. Only because someone does us the honor of accepting.*" Give the coaches around you the opportunity to serve. Spiritual directors and your religious community can provide you with the support you need to heal and advocate for you through prayer and personal sacrifice. Counselors can help you to mitigate the mental stress that your spiritual burden is causing. Teachers across a wide variety of subjects can help you to engage therapeutically in the arts which can be incredibly valuable in expressing and coping with your pain. Finally, health coaches can take the reins of your fitness and nutrition by providing you with realistic, thoughtful programs to help you achieve better physical wellness as you focus your energies in other areas.

Chapter 6
Living in the Past

"You cannot pray your way out of a situation you behaved your way into."
– Andy Stanley

Past behavior may be the best predictor of future behavior, but it doesn't have to be. It is, however, important to value both our personal past and our collective past in order to learn from our mistakes and make corrections for the future. We make our decisions based on what we know through our past experiences and we become practiced in behaviors that we incorporate into our daily lives without much effort. We call these behaviors habits, which can sometimes be a physical manifestation of living in the past if we are not intentional and responsible about which ones we keep and which ones we give up. Webster's defines a 'habit' as "an acquired behavior pattern, regularly followed until it has become almost involuntary." Habits are a part of our past, since that is where they originate. A healthy habit should be embraced and maintained, but a habit that is no longer beneficial or was detrimental from the beginning needs to be conquered. The past is also where we get many of our excuses. We use these excuses to justify our resistance to change, and in doing so, we turn unwillingness into inability. Living in the past makes it difficult to overcome our own guilt and failure, and it also makes it difficult to forgive others in order to move on. For a coach, helping an individual identify and overcome bad habits is crucial for long-term success and wellness. Living in the past is a state of mind that does little to help us reach our goals.

Several years ago, I started listening to Andy Stanley via his app called 'Your Move.' He organizes his Sunday preaching into a four-or-so part series, and the themes are listed on the app where you can listen to them at your convenience. A counselor once recommended the app to me, and I began going through the entire catalogue during my long commutes. Andy has a great way of explaining scripture that is profoundly simple. Each series he develops is essentially a self-help topic applicable to today, and he preaches on the Christian values and biblical foundation for the advice that he offers. After listening to all of the content available on the app, it was not surprising that it had been recommended to me by a counselor. Andy doesn't speak in the same way that many of my favorite theologians write, he speaks like a therapist. He speaks like a coach. It is clear to me that he has a genuine desire to see people thrive physically, mentally, and spiritually according to God's will. His lectures are often as applicable to nonbelievers as they are to Christians because what he does so well is to point out how our holistic wellness is jeopardized when we do not behave as we were intended to behave.

In addition to the theological reasoning behind his advice, some of the most powerful coaching he provides is rooted in simple common sense. The quote I shared at the beginning of this chapter is one of my favorites. While I am absolutely a big believer in prayer and its impact on body, mind, and spirit, far too often we speak our intentions and desires to God and then just sit around waiting for magic to happen. You cannot pray your way out of a situation that you behaved your way into. Andy follows up this great thought by saying, "But you can follow Jesus out." As I write this book, it is becoming more and more evident to me that Jesus was, and is, the ultimate coach. As Christians, we believe that the Son of Man came to teach us how to act and to set an example for us to follow. He provided instruction and clarification and then demonstrated his advice through his own actions and behavior. What strikes me about Jesus the Coach is the way he meets each person where they are. In every encounter, he encourages and welcomes, but he also challenges. Too often, we equate love with acceptance, but they are absolutely not the same thing. Each of us deserves to be accepted for who we are, but real love will never perpetuate stagnation. Because Jesus loves each person he meets, he accepts them but then challenges them to continue to grow in truth through effort and discipline.

St. Teresa of Calcutta says a great thing about prayer: "I used to think that prayer changed things. Now I know that prayer changes us, and we change things." Her words are an articulate reflection on the belief that prayer is not a transaction but rather a relationship with the Living God. It is a good thing to pray for that which concerns you, but it is even better to pray for wisdom, understanding, discipline, and love. When we become more aware of ourselves and more aware of God's will, we are empowered to break the habits that chain us to the past. Living in the past is a very passive way to exist. Positive changes towards holistic wellness require more than the purchase of a treadmill or diet program, they require discipline and desire. Each of us should desire to be a little healthier in mind, body, and spirit than we have been in our past. Andy's quote is relevant even to those who do not consider themselves religious—just replace 'pray' with 'wish.' You cannot wish your way out of your circumstances, and to remain where you are and wish that that the past had been different is a tragic waste of time. We all know that physical wellness requires work, and there is no prayer or wish that transforms us into fit, healthy, energetic people. We've all behaved our way to some degree of 'unfit' at some point (or maybe many points) of our lives, and each new day is an opportunity to behave better.

Physical habits are incredibly difficult to overcome, especially when they are indulgent habits that produce temporary chemical highs in our brains. Smoking, alcohol, sugar, and even smart phones flood the brain with dopamine which is the primary 'feel-good' chemical and creates the association between the stimulus and the subsequent effect on the brain. At the very least, this repetitive behavior and physical reaction leads to a behavior that is somewhat challenging to avoid. In more severe cases, this cause and effect can create an addiction. Neither of these scenarios comes as a surprise to most, however, the genetic predisposition to an already dysfunctional chemical process can set off a chain reaction of feelings and behaviors that are more than difficult to overcome. This is why it is important to acknowledge that you were, in fact, designed to be well. Each of us has challenges that must be overcome, but we do not need to accept dysfunction or give into hopelessness.

'It's too late' and 'It's just the way it is' are two common phrases I hear when I am working with a patient or client. This is another example of unhealthy acceptance and of living in the past. Physical wellness is so often sabotaged by a belief that being well isn't an option. After receiving a diagnosis or suffering for years with a chronic condition, many people believe that all that is left is to accept an inevitable decline. I can tell you, as a therapist and health coach, that this is not true. I have seen firsthand, the potential for wellness that remains despite chronic disease or traumatic injury, and I know that the events of the past do not have to ruin your future. We are designed to persevere in our pursuit of truth and fulfillment of purpose. Do not believe the lie that you cannot get better. While there may be permanent conditions that cannot be ignored, there is always room to improve your health.

Perhaps the challenges to your mental wellness are the most difficult to overcome when it comes to living in the past. We've all behaved our way into bad situations. When we overeat, we gain weight. When we overspend, we fall into debt. When we hold onto grudges, we allow anger to make decisions for us. When we give pieces of ourselves away to those who do not have our best interests at heart, we are left feeling incomplete. And this is when the dreaded cycle of living in the past gets a grip on us. I call this the Self Cycle. The Self Cycle is a miserable circle of self-pity and self-loathing. We pity ourselves and resent life for being unfair, which justifies our self-indulgent behavior. Sometimes, it's something simple like having a bad day at work and using that as an excuse to indulge in too much food, skip a workout, drink more than we should, or lash out at a loved one. Sometimes, it's more serious, and we use our past circumstances to justify inappropriate or hateful behavior, acceptance of unnecessary charity or consistent excessive indulgence in things that are detrimental to our health. This is victim behavior.

The Forever Victim is a tough person to coach because their self-pity ultimately masks self-punishment. Believing the lie that you are a perpetual victim of circumstance is a self-imposed limitation on success. While the Forever Victim will often stay stagnant in the self-pity phase of the Self Cycle, others will experience the pendulum swinging to self-loathing. Instead of hearing an inner voice that blames the world around you, you begin to hear a self-hating voice. The voice that says that you earned your problems, that your circumstances are your fault, and that you don't deserve to do or to have any better. By chaining yourself to your past through either of these dysfunctional thought patterns, you will burden one or more components of self.

Relationships also have a dynamic impact on our ability to progress beyond our past habits and circumstances. The people in our lives, especially those with whom we have a long history, can intentionally or unintentionally prevent us from letting go of the past in pursuit of becoming the people we are meant to be. Harmful relationships have an obvious negative impact by actively encouraging unhealthy behaviors. These relationships can range from friendships heavily weighted in indulgent or sinful activities, to genuinely abusive partners that cause injury and illness to all components of self. These can be people who encourage you to drink too much, use drugs, or embrace lifestyle habits that detract from our design. They can also be people who encourage us to gossip, harbor resentments, or judge other people. Typically, the stronger the relationship, the harder the pushback when you attempt to initiate a change. People will often perceive your attempts at self-improvement as rejection which leads to a whole host of unhealthy relationship dynamics. Qualified counselors are the best resource for coping with these issues, and even good relationships can benefit from therapeutic intervention.

Sometimes, knowing someone very intimately can facilitate a stagnant environment that prevents growth and achievement. When two people know each other especially well, they can often anticipate what the other person will think or do or say in a given situation. They become well acquainted with each other's habits and abilities and are rarely surprised by the other person's decisions or behavior. Unfortunately, this can also subtly influence each person by preventing them from making positive changes. Sometimes, this may come from fear that the progress of a loved one will cause them to leave the relationship behind, in other cases, maybe jealousy fuels the resistance. But a truly great relationship should inspire each person to continue to improve and become more and more well in all areas of life. Unhealthy relationships, especially those with a long history, are an example of unbalanced mental burden and need to be ended or, at least, professionally treated before you can pursue the condition of wellness that supports you on your journey.

Good relationships with the potential to inadvertently sabotage your efforts need to be modified so that they can grow along with you as you become healthier instead of keeping you tethered to the past. It is important to look at both sides of this issue when you assess this area of your own life. What relationships in your life make it difficult for you to be healthy? It could be a spouse, partner, parent, friend, or authority figure. But also consider this: are you preventing anyone in your life from improving themselves? Do you enable any of your family members or friends? Do you look the other way when they engage in unhealthy behaviors? Or worse still, do you discourage positive changes in their life because you're afraid of how that will affect you? If you can honestly answer both sides of the issue, not only will you become healthier, but your relationships and the people in your life you can join you in leaving the past behind and become healthier along with you.

What does living in the past look like spiritually? This is a question that I'm not sure I'd ever be able to answer. But I can tell you that anything that chains you to your past is not something you should be carrying around with you. St. Teresa of Calcutta shared so much wisdom while she was alive, and another of my favorite quotes from her is: "Do not let the past disturb you, just leave everything in the Sacred Heart and begin again with joy." Each day arrives with the right amount of resource and the right amount of struggle. To carry the burdens of the past from one day to the next is not something we were designed to do well. Whether Christian or not, healthy spiritual practice should encourage you to let go of past failures. My very adorable niece, who isn't a fan of sleep, was lying next to me one night after my own children had fallen asleep and was chatting away, throwing all kinds of four-year-old existential questions my way:

"Aunt Erin, where do the months go when we are finished with them?"

"They go into the past."

"But where do we put them in the past?"

"We put them into books."

"Why?"

"So we can read about them if we want to."

The past is a valuable resource for us all. We must look back to see where we came from and to learn from what has happened, but once we have, we need to close the book. For a long time, I had difficulty seeing deep meaning in the Transfiguration passage in the Bible. I understood that the two apostles who accompanied Jesus were witnesses to a vision of Moses and Elijah and briefly experienced the radiance of Jesus's divinity. For me, this didn't seem that informative. They were already pretty clear on who Jesus was, and while I'm sure it was an incredible experience, I didn't take anything away from that passage that I hadn't already learned from somewhere else in the Bible (a common and always incorrect sentiment!). As a Catholic, it is a mystery of the rosary to be meditated upon, and I'll admit, for many years, meditating on that particular story wasn't especially inspiring to me. Thankfully, I am beginning to understand it more clearly, though I am sure I have a long way to go. Up on that mountain, those apostles were witness not only to what Jesus truly looked like in all of His simultaneous humanity and divinity, but I believe they may have also seen themselves as they were designed to be. I believe that the Transfiguration reveals to us what and who we are as members of the collective Body of Christ and outside of the constraints of time and flesh. I believe it reveals to us the radiant image that we were created in the likeness of and how God desires for us to be once again when we are reunited with Him. Your past and my past leave dark marks and scars that cover the truth of who we are. Meditating on the past beliefs and experiences that have contributed to an unhealthy mind, body, and soul is the first step in learning from your spiritual past and leaving it behind, right where it belongs, so that you can begin each day again with joy.

How can a coach help?

There are three crucial pillars of effective health coaching that must guide interventions in order to achieve optimal wellness. Root Cause Reversal is the first pillar and addresses the problems of living in the past. Root Cause Reversal deals with the issues that have been building over time, manifesting in various symptoms and ultimately preventing meaningful wellness. Today's healthcare delivery models do not adequately seek out root causes and rarely attempt to reverse the subsequent damage. Typically, when a patient is seen during a sick visit or an emergency visit, the primary complaint is addressed and the doctor evaluates the cause of the presenting illness after receiving the results of relevant tests. The patient is treated based on the diagnosis and, sometimes, for other worrisome or bothersome symptoms. For more serious illness or injuries or for chronic conditions with acute exacerbation, patients may need to be followed by a team of nurses or therapists to rehabilitate to what is called a 'functional baseline.' This is the level of function that a person is presumed to be able to consistently maintain after they have received treatment. Usually, the baseline level of function is based on what the individual was most recently able to do just before they experienced an increase in symptoms. This is not a bad practice, and it is what needs to be done in order for someone to 'return to normal.' However, far too often, these events leave people with either new diagnoses to cope with or new challenges to overcome to achieve wellness. Without taking the opportunity to look deeper into the past at the true genesis of the symptoms and dysfunction, symptoms may return or new illness may develop. This is where health coaching comes in! By following the principles of Root Cause Reversal, a qualified health coach can assess the unseen and make meaningful and personalized changes to your lifestyle, all the while utilizing the valuable principles of coaching to help ensure your success.

As we discussed throughout this chapter, there are other coaches you should consider seeking help from when attempting to overcome the challenges of your past. Integrative health practitioners are an excellent resource for looking into underlying medical conditions and seeking treatment for improper gene function. Licensed counselors are an incredibly helpful resource in learning the tools necessary to set healthy boundaries in relationships and for learning effective communication skills for all different types of relationships. And finally, your everyday coaches. We haven't mentioned the value of the skills of specific coaches that work every day helping people to achieve competency in all sorts of areas. Sometimes, learning something new or breaking through a personal plateau can be monumental in stepping out of the past. Music teachers, sport trainers, and professional coaches covering a vast area of expertise can help you to develop new skills and to focus on positive personal growth.

Do not let the past disturb you.

Chapter 7
Living Only for the Now

"Take care of your body as if you were going to live forever, and take care of your soul as if you were going to die tomorrow."
– St Augustine of Hippo

Living in the present is a good thing, let's make that clear before we dive into this chapter. God asks us to leave the past with him and to trust Him with our futures. We are to ask Him for our daily bread and to focus on the tasks at hand. Yoga is a practice that unites movement and breath and philosophically encourages practitioners to empty the mind of past and future worries and focus only on the present. But we are not talking about a healthy sense of living in the moment with mindfulness and intention. In this chapter, we will consider the issues of living only for the now. Instant gratification is the immediate accommodation of impulse or desire. It does not take into thoughtful consideration the potential consequences of getting what we want. It does not consider the effects on tomorrow because the desire for convenience and pleasure overpower our wisdom and patience. Avoidance is an altogether different way to live in the present without concern for the future.

Avoidance comes from laziness or from fear. It refuses to deal effectively with the issues of the present, hoping that they will go away by themselves. It kicks today's problems down the road using whatever excuses are available.

"Do whatever makes you happy!" It sounds like such an innocent and positive sentiment. Versions of this phrase are seen on t-shirts, coffee mugs, and social media every day. Doing whatever makes you happy often means doing whatever makes you happy in the moment. It can most certainly be argued that doing what makes you happy is a valid and positive way to live. For example, if the things that make you happy are growing in love for God and neighbor, caring for yourself and others, and serving the world around you, I suppose you should continue to do what makes you happy. The tricky thing is sometimes these are the things that make us happy, especially when we are feeling well, but all of us have a selfish side to battle that desires things far less altruistic. It is the definition of 'happiness' though, that is really at the heart of the conversation here.

Over the last several years, the themes of happiness and joy have frequently been highlighted in some very popular TED talks. Major universities have conducted studies on the science of happiness while writers and philosophers explore the intangible secrets to being happy. There are identifiable themes found in the results of these studies, and these same themes are woven throughout less scientific discussions on the topic. Gratitude and service are two of these themes, and their existence in the foundation of true happiness is widely recognized. Whether by secular or religious groups, many studies have shown that people who are mindful in their gratitude and who use their time to volunteer and serve others, consistently report greater and more sustained levels of happiness.

C.S. Lewis has written much on this topic and shares his belief that those who fulfill that for which they were created are the ones who find true joy. Unfortunately, this is not the meaningful happiness that our modern culture is usually referring to when we hear this cliché: "Do more of what makes you happy!" We are being both subtly and overtly coerced into buying more, eating more, spending more, and wasting more. The happiness that we are constantly encouraged to seek has to do with feeding our impulses and avoiding anything that makes us unhappy or uncomfortable. And it is becoming more and more acceptable to do whatever it is that makes us happy, to the detriment of our own integrity as well as at the cost of other people's freedom. Sometimes, the thing we want in the moment is something simple. Sometimes, we want dessert or another glass of wine or to call in sick. None of these things on their own is evil. Problems arise when they become patterns of behavior or when they begin to dominate better, more disciplined behavior. This is an issue in all areas of wellness. Doing more of what makes us 'happy' often comes at the cost of doing something that is actually good for us. In the moment, I feel happy, but in the long run, I am less healthy. Instant gratification fills our bodies, minds, and souls with things that may not be inherently bad, but when they fill us up, we have no room left for what is truly good.

I have learned over the years, that if you come across a scripture verse that you don't like, you should stick with it until you understand it better. One of the earliest examples of this in my own life is from Jeremiah. In chapter 17:9, we read: "The heart is deceitful above all things and beyond cure. Who can understand it?" In my early twenties, this verse struck me as contrary to so many verses in the Bible about love and about goodness in our hearts. This is one of the verses that people are acknowledging when they say things like: "You should thank God for the things He doesn't give you and the prayers He doesn't answer." No one who is going through a tough time in their life, or who has been intensely hoping for something, wants to get advice like that. Other times, it isn't the frustration of not having access to the thing we want, but the struggle to deny ourselves something that we know isn't good for us even though it is right there for the taking. What this verse in Jeremiah is telling us is that we can fool ourselves, and often times, we don't really even know what it is that we truly desire. Each of us has a time in our life that we can look back on and see that something we wanted so badly (a relationship, a job, a big purchase) was definitely not a good idea and something that we no longer have any desire for whatsoever. But desire is a powerful feeling, and at the time, no one could have convinced us that one day we would feel differently. Even after I had accepted that our hearts are not always right, I still felt frustrated at the cruel mechanism at work. How much more difficult is it to make sound decisions when your heart is not cooperating? In Christianity, this is when the principles of prayer and communion with God are the answer to the problem. In the practice and pursuit of holistic health, I would elaborate on those principles to include seeking the support of your core wellness tribe and relying on your coaches to help you navigate your temptations and weaknesses.

It is easy to see how instant gratification sabotages our pursuit of physical wellness. Over indulging in food, alcohol, and sleep are obvious examples. Caving into other physical desires can also have a negative impact on our holistic wellness. One of the many studies citing the negative effects of casual sexual encounters looked at three different age groups and the effects of promiscuity. The study and article titled *The Relationship Between Multiple Sex Partners and Anxiety, Depression and Substance Abuse Disorders*, by Ramrakha, Paul, Bell, Dickson, Moffitt, and Caspi concluded that across each group, significantly higher rates of substance abuse and depression were found in correlation with the number of partners and encounters a person had. But despite secular scientific research that warns of these consequences, 'sexual freedom' is still highly valued by our culture and is a prime example of succumbing to instant gratification. By giving into immediate physical desires, mental and spiritual wellness suffers.

It is most often the pursuit of some type of physical pleasure that leads to instant gratification. It is typically the drive of the Id and pursuit of physical pleasure that ends up having a negative effect on the other two components of self. Obedience and discipline are the antidotes to instant gratification. Obedience considers wisdom, accountability, and consequence, while discipline practices positive behaviors in pursuit of healthy habits. This is intelligent and mature behavior whether you consider yourself to be religious or not. Taking your time to consider the potential negative consequences before engaging in any behavior will protect you from harming all components of self. As Christians, we are fortunate to have a guide to keep us on course when temptations are tough to overcome. In health coaching, the accountability to our tribe and the support of our coaches can help us to live up to our commitments and get through tempting times without undoing our progress and sabotaging our long-term wellness.

Avoidance is the more solemn sister of Instant Gratification. Avoidance is a resistance or refusal to confront and treat the issues that are actively preventing us from being healthy in any or all components of self. Where instant gratification seeks immediate reward, avoidance seeks to prevent immediate punishment. Of the two negative ways to live only for the now, I would argue that avoidance is an even stronger driver than instant gratification. While we may be able to build up some level of discipline against things that are not good for us, avoiding the pains and efforts of confronting today's problems is a discipline much harder to come by. Health coaches struggle to help their clients win this battle every day. Avoidance is excellent at providing us with excuses and inspiring us to procrastinate. When we chose to avoid doing that which will make us healthy, simply because it isn't convenient, fun, or interesting, it is laziness that drives our behavior. When the stakes are higher and the symptoms of physical, mental, or spiritual dysfunction are more serious, it is usually fear that prevents us from confronting our problems and working towards solutions. Both laziness and fear are difficult to overcome, and all of us need help to conquer our avoidance.

The pursuit of physical wellness is frequently derailed by avoidance. One popular manifestation of avoidance is to procrastinate the pursuit of wellness altogether. Fitness and healthy eating are frequently put off until Monday, the ever-popular magic start day for wellness. Monday arrives, but avoidance keeps plenty of excuses on hand to push wellness goals off for another week. Whether a stressful day at work, an event with unexpected tempting food, a late night that leads to sleeping late or any type of physical discomfort, we put off until tomorrow what we could do today because it just isn't something we're looking forward to doing. This avoidance becomes an even bigger issue when we put off important medical tests or doctor's visits. Of course, to be fair, laziness isn't always the motivator for neglecting our health and avoiding new wellness plans. Most people know what it's like to juggle long workweeks, care for a home, care for children and possibly older family members, or prepare for a major life transition. These are valid excuses for delaying our wellness goals, except that they aren't.

Remember back to the beginning of the book, when we explored the true purpose of wellness. Wellness isn't the goal, it is the *condition necessary for achieving your goals and living well for yourself and others.* Being burdened and busy is actually a great reason to carve out time to confront the issues of your physical health that are impacting your ability to achieve holistic wellness. While putting your own needs below the needs of your loved ones is a gracious and loving attitude to have, it can also boomerang back to cause bigger problems for you and for them. By avoiding the medical exam or diagnostic visit with your health practitioner, you could be putting yourself at greater risk for serious health conditions. There are many health conditions that are easy to address in their earliest stages, that become far more challenging by the time you become actively symptomatic. Fear is the other major motivator for avoidance, and anyone who struggles with even mild hypochondriasis knows the internal struggle between wanting an explanation for your symptoms and wanting them to just disappear. Health coaches and other members of your wellness team can provide you with excellent support in helping you navigate the process of diagnosing and treatment planning.

Avoidance can also have a major impact on our mental and spiritual wellbeing. In my own experience, the avoidance of dealing with components of my mental wellness has had a far greater negative impact on my health than any of my unhealthy physical habits. I have had more than one period in my life when I refused to confront my financial struggles and ended up in far greater debt than if I had just asked for help and guidance to begin with. This caused mental and physical anxiety and had an unfair impact on people in my life who shouldn't have had to suffer the consequences of my avoidance. The inevitable outcome of avoidance is regret because the thing about kicking your problems down the road is that they will be there waiting for you at one point or another.

Perhaps one of the most devastating examples of avoidance leading to regret is the procrastination of reconciliation. Nobody wins when we refuse to reconcile with the people we love after arguments or hardship. And because none of us will live forever, there will come a time for all of us when it is too late for forgiveness and reunion.

Our avoidance of reconciliation with God is no different. Wasting years of our lives angry with God or a religious institution does little to heal our wounds or help us to be healthy. Confronting the physical, mental, and spiritual burdens that intimidate us the most can have a dramatic impact on our holistic wellness. There is a virtue to help us overcome our desire to avoid. Just as obedience and discipline helps us to overcome the desire for instant gratification, humility is the antidote for avoidance. Of course, humility isn't a virtue that most of us are quick to adopt, but true humility guides us to live in the now with discipline, wisdom, and joy. Humility is not only an awareness of your faults, but also of your value. Humility encourages us to seek help from our creator and from each other. We seek help not only because we cannot overcome all our problems on our own, but also because we deserve help!

"For God has not given us a spirit of fear or timidity but of power, love, and self-discipline." (2 Tim1:7)

We were designed to not only be well, but to pursue wellness through courage, love, and obedience.

How can a coach help?

In the last chapter, we defined the first pillar of effective health coaching: Root Cause Reversal. This pillar deals with the problems of the past and an individual's history. The second pillar focuses on the present and overcoming the pitfalls of instant gratification and avoidance. Active Symptom Treatment seeks to evaluate and address the challenges to a person's physical, mental, and spiritual health manifesting in active symptoms. For those who have stabilized after an illness or injury and no longer require the services of licensed therapy or intensive medical intervention, coaching is a highly effective way to continue to make slow but steady progress towards a healthier baseline. Qualified health coaches have the necessary tools to greatly increase the likelihood of more permanent success and decrease the risk of relapse. For those who have not experienced a serious illness or injury, but who have identified mild or moderate symptoms of dysfunction, a health coach can devise a plan to address current symptoms and avoid future disease. Active symptoms need to be explored through a holistic lens because, often times, seemingly unrelated symptoms can actually lead to a more accurate diagnosis than when addressing individual complaints.

No pillar is more important than the others, but sometimes Active Symptom Treatment requires the most time initially because the nature of the symptoms demand attention. The process of assessing and recovering from active symptoms is usually an easier sell to people struggling with physical wellness because their conditions are often preventing them from optimal function. Most people are motivated by the opportunity to have less pain, have more energy, or get better sleep. The challenge to a health coach dealing with active symptoms is devising a plan that is both effective and least disruptive. In therapy, we use a term called 'least restrictive' to explain a level of assistance or a living arrangement that allows an individual to maintain as much freedom and independence as possible while also remaining safe. In wellness coaching, it is important to create a plan that is both highly effective and also has the smallest possible impact on a client's life and therefore is least disruptive to their current lifestyle. People are more likely to follow a plan with manageable changes than something that causes a major disruption to multiple areas of their life all at once.

Besides health coaches, counselors and other types of advisors are also valuable in helping us to overcome the behaviors that keep us living naively in the now. In addition to these other coaches that we have mentioned, addiction counselors and debt relief advisors have a lot to offer when dealing with the challenges of the present.

Living in the moment is a good thing, but not at the cost of tomorrow. The practice of mindfulness cultivates an awareness of body, mind, and spirit so that we can confront the burdens and habits that prevent us from being well and serving our greater purpose. St. Augustine writes that we should take care of our bodies as if we were going to live forever. This is why we cannot avoid confronting the problems of today. Physical and mental wellness issues require our attention. As a therapist and health coach, I see patients every single day neglect their health issues, refusing to acknowledge the current and future consequences of doing so. Augustine goes on to encourage us to care for our souls as if we will die tomorrow. And this is why we cannot allow the desire for instant gratification to make decisions for us. Today is a gift and what we do with it determines what we will encounter tomorrow.

Chapter 8
Living in the Future

"The future depends on what we do in the present."
– Gandhi

How we see the future says a lot about who we are, and our perspective on wellness says a lot about how we see the future. In the beginning of the book, I mentioned the importance of goal setting in my role as an occupational therapist. Goal setting is, by nature, a guess at the future based on the facts of the past and condition of the present. As a therapist and health coach, I can honestly say that I approach each new case with optimism. I believe that people can and will get better, and if at first they don't believe it themselves, I always have enough faith to get both of us started. If I am being totally honest, it's probably the fact that I feel competitive enough for the both of us! I think the best coaches are made up of equal parts feisty competitor and compassionate nurturer. But the success of any therapist or coach ultimately depends on the willingness and determination of the person they are working with.

In western medicine, there is a largely passive approach to being a patient. People go to doctors and share their primary complaints. Doctors choose tests, determine diagnoses, and prescribe generally passive treatment. This is not because doctors do not wish to coach their patients to greater health, but because it is outside of their power to force a patient to make lifestyle changes. Our current healthcare system leaves little time for physicians to coach their patients towards holistic health, and they often meet resistance from patients when they try. Mental health practitioners, especially those working in addiction, can face similar challenges. Even spiritual wellness suffers from a passive, unwilling attitude from those seeking guidance and advice. Over and over, churches are criticized for not 'modernizing' because doctrine is inconvenient for those seeking acceptance instead of truth. To pursue truth and achieve our best potential, we must be willing to work and to make changes within all components of self.

Over the years, I have observed four general perspectives on the future from the clients that I have served. The first is the Optimist, and is as easy to define as you'd think. These are the people that generally see the glass half-full as the saying goes. This is, of course, a great attitude to have and typically an easy client to work with. The Optimist believes that they can get well, that their circumstances will improve and that the future is bright. Unfortunately, this does not automatically translate into success because optimism does not equal hard work. In addition to believing that good things are possible, one also must be willing to take the steps necessary to improve.

In the pursuit of physical wellness, optimism without commitment is common. One reason for this seems to be that people tend to believe that they have plenty of time. While working in rehabilitation centers, this was a common theme during discharge planning meetings. Patients who suffered an illness or injury would participate in therapy and receive necessary medical care. In preparation for their return home, we would make recommendations to decrease their risk of relapse or to prevent a new injury. Time after time, patients would refuse our advice insisting that "everything would be fine" or "maybe one day I'll make those changes, but I don't need them yet." Those who chose not to comply with at least some of our suggestions were far more likely to end up in the hospital again.

We spoke about avoidance in the last chapter, and I've discovered that many people mask avoidance with faux optimism, choosing to believe that everything will work out, but refusing to do what is necessary to help themselves. This same misguided attitude effects those of us who haven't yet suffered a major illness or injury. Whether it is the weight we know we should lose, the substance we know we shouldn't be taking, or the exercise we never get around to, optimism can sometimes enable us to put off until tomorrow what it is we should be doing today. In 17 years, I have yet to work with a patient who didn't regret neglecting their health. No one ever says that if they could go back and do it again, they'd happily make all the same unhealthy choices.

Blind optimism can have a major effect on our mental health as well. Perhaps it's a bad relationship that we hope will one day become healthy again, even though we haven't sought any professional advice or support. Or maybe it's a debt that we are sure we'll be able to pay off someday even though we aren't doing anything to resolve it today. Or maybe we believe that by simply 'being a good person' or 'accepting Jesus as our Savior,' we have secured our place in heaven and no longer have any spiritual growth to worry about. In any case, it is a beautiful thing to believe the best in others and to be hopeful about the future, but that doesn't take the place of effort and planning.

Thanks to the phenomenal scientific advancements in epigenetics, we are able to make highly educated guesses about what the future of our health will look like. The Optimist is a great candidate for coaching according to a personalized plan guided by the pillars of professional health coaching because their positive outlook has already won half the battle. A health coach, or any other type of coach, should provide adequate support to take the burden of planning and organizing off of the optimist so that they can use their full energy to focus on adapting to new and healthy behaviors.

The second perspective on the future is the Aggressive Optimist. This person takes the pendulum from the side of the avoidance clear over to the other extreme of intense control. The Aggressive Optimist also chooses to believe that, in general, good things will happen but takes the weight of the world on their shoulders and tries to control each and every aspect of both the present and the future. While their willingness to put in the effort is a useful quality, the obsession with control is detrimental to mind, body, and spirit. The Aggressive Optimist can be easy to work with as long as they are in control of their goals, but often, it is their own intensity that sabotages their success. Those who view the future this way often lack patience with themselves and others. Working with these clients, I usually worry that they will overdo it and potentially set themselves back because they have pushed their minds and bodies too hard.

The Aggressive Optimist is often a leader by nature and can therefore have a difficult time accepting help from others. Physically, this can lead to many health issues related to wear and tear. Pushing the body beyond its limits can increase the body's stress responses which then causes an increase in inflammation. Inflammation is at the heart of almost every illness and non-traumatic injury. For someone inclined to this perspective on the future, it is important to help them see the value in a balanced approach to physical wellness, including adequate rest, leisure, and well-paced goals. This perspective on the future can also lead to workaholic behavior.

In the fourth chapter, we discussed the effects of an unbalance pursuit of one or more components of self, an Aggressive Optimist is likely to have difficulty avoiding this imbalance. At the heart of this imbalance is the need for certainty. This need for certainty is rooted in fear and is not unique to this group of people, but their approach to handling fear and anxiety is to control as many variables as they can. It is important for each of us to separate this fear into two categories to continue our journey to wellness and purpose. There is a normal fear of the future and of the unknown that we must acknowledge and then let go of. This is, of course, easier said than done, and something we all have to confront regularly. Then there is the fear of failure, and this is the driver for the Aggressive Optimist that can be useful if it is kept in check. I once heard actor Kevin Hart say, "Fear of failure isn't a bad thing, it just means you really want to succeed." This is true, but it is also important to acknowledge if this sentiment is what drives you. Those who view the future this way need the support of their tribe to channel their fear of failure into a well-balanced pursuit of holistic health.

There is little that we can be sure of when we consider the future, but there is great value in honestly assessing what it is we can do and in making plans to do those things well. Recently, I was reflecting on the personality traits of the people who inspire me the most, and I came up with a simple description: scrappy people with absurd goals who are nice to everyone. These are my favorite kinds of people. For me, these people maintain a generally optimistic perspective on the future and understand that lofty goals are important and inspiring because we were designed to do great things! But our optimism must also be balanced by the acceptance of the things that are outside of our control as well as by a genuine concern for the people around us. Measurable progress is important to the Aggressive Optimist when setting goals for the future, and good coaches can help those with this perspective by reminding them of the intangibles and the value of balance.

The third perspective on the future is the Pessimist. This, of course, is the glass-half-empty view of the future. The Pessimist believes that good things are possible and happen all the time, just not for them. In my experience working with patients, the Pessimist is someone who has been carrying around an unbalanced burden of one or more components of self that has led to holistic illness. We explored the unbalanced burden on self in chapter five, looking at the effects of illnesses or injuries to mind, body, or spirit that may not be our fault but have become our problem. I believe that each of us has a set of internal and external challenges to overcome, and the ability to choose positive thinking over negative thinking takes more work for some people than it does for others. But I do not believe that anyone is born a hopeless pessimist because, of course, I believe we were designed to be well.

Researchers have found some markers in the brain that indicate a tendency towards negative thinking, but there are also many studies that indicate that people more often view themselves and their circumstances to be even better than objective measures would suggest. So, what is at the heart of a Pessimist's view of the future? The same fear and anxiety that all of us struggle to overcome. The Pessimist channels this fear and anxiety into negative thinking and into something that psychologists call 'defensive pessimism.' This is a defense mechanism that pessimists use to avoid disappointment. By setting expectations low and refusing to allow hopeful optimism to settle in, people with this view of the future protect themselves from the pain of failure. The Pessimist has likely given a good amount of thought to possible outcomes of the future and feels overwhelmed by the mountain of seemingly impossible tasks that lie ahead.

Recognizing the fear and anxiety that each of us faces, which makes us feel isolated and, at times, hopeless, is the first step in retraining our brains to choose positive thinking. One of the initial challenges in working with a Pessimist is getting through a hard exterior. Defensive pessimism often presents with a toughness that can come across as rude or even aggressive. In my own personal experience, receiving the resistance and complaints of a Pessimist with calmness and generosity can help build rapport and encourage people to consider the possibility of a healthy future. Respectfully allowing a person with this view of the future to express their fears and concerns can be really useful in building trust that supports a health coaching dynamic.

The final perspective on the future is the Passive Pessimist. This is the most challenging client to serve in a rehabilitative setting and likely declines any sort of voluntary coaching. While the Pessimist wants success and wellness, but feels angry or frustrated at not being able to attain it, the Passive Pessimist does not have an accessible desire to improve. This is a complicated perspective on the future and one that is difficult to overcome. Passive pessimism sees both the present and the future as more bad than good with no hope for improvement. This is despair masked as apathy. I do not believe that we were designed as apathetic beings, but often, it is easier to deny our thoughts and feelings than it is to deal with them. People with this perspective on the future essentially 'give up' on not only wellness but on seeking truth and fulfilling purpose altogether. Physically, this manifests in more obvious ways. A passive pessimist is certainly not going to be outrunning or walking or going to the gym. Some Passive Pessimists may overeat and some may not want to eat at all. Mentally, this perspective on the future can have other devastating effects. While some people struggling with this mindset may neglect their responsibilities altogether, others will do what is necessary to survive and will simply go through the motions without joy or satisfaction. Passive Pessimists are not ready to plan for the future and are not, likely, even giving it much consideration. These are likely some of the people we spoke about before who need a chance to lie on the mat and have their burdens carried by others for a while. Passive pessimism is a lonely state of mind, and being close to someone suffering from this sense of isolation can be frustrating. It is very difficult to help someone who refuses to help themselves. Remember, as often as you can, to pray for the lonely and the hopeless and continue to invite them into your core wellness tribe. In practice, Passive Pessimists may initially require more clinical intervention before they are ready to work with a health coach.

So, which one are you? The reality is most of us have experienced feelings from each of these categories at one point or another when considering our futures. At times, things are good and we have little concern for what is to come, at other times, we are motivated but perhaps too focused on having things our way. And all of us have been defeated at one point or another, filling us with fear, disappointment, anxiety, or anger. These are normal perspectives on the future, but none of them serves the condition of holistic wellness. Remember that this world is that boat we're all in together and that it is heading closer and closer to our ultimate destination. These feelings create the fog that prevents us from seeing clearly the future that we are working towards.

There is a better perspective from which to see the future, and it is how each of us should approach today, tomorrow, and our own personal pursuit of wellness. We were designed to be Intentional Servants. Instead of looking at the future as the Optimist, Aggressive Optimist, Pessimist, or Passive Pessimist, we should pursue the condition of health as Intentional Servants. There is a way to work for a great tomorrow without losing sight of today, and it all comes back to the deathbed question which is the ultimate view of the future. What story do you want to look back on when it is all over? When you can answer that question, you can begin to live each day in a way that helps to write that story. Your future self will likely regret missed opportunities, pursuing only that which was self-serving or holding onto anger and grudges. In contrast, your future self will appreciate the effort you put into having a body, mind, and soul healthy enough to experience life the way you were designed to live it.

How can a coach help?

The principle of Root Cause Reversal addresses the past by looking at our own personal history and problem solving to optimize the function of our mind, body, and spirit. We've discussed how this pillar improves our health and removes the causes of our dysfunction. Active Symptom Treatment is the second pillar and focuses on the most significant problems of the present and how to heal illness or injury to any component of self. In this chapter, we've discussed the issues we face in preparing for the future and how to live well now in order to live well later. The third and final pillar for effective health coaching that addresses the future is Longevity Planning. Without a comprehensive, holistic approach to long-term planning, we cannot expect our future to turn out the way we hope. Longevity Planning does not seek to control every aspect of the future because none of us knows what will happen tomorrow or how long we can expect to live. Instead, it uses the information available to us and the wisdom of others to guide our actions today to avoid unnecessary illness, injury, or financial hardship down the road. This requires having a team of coaches and a desire to live well for yourself and for others. Financial planners are probably the most well-known group of coaches related to longevity planning, but in recent years, the value of adding the expertise of a professional health coach is gaining in popularity. In addition, it is important to have a doctor who considers both the true causes of your symptoms as well as your own personal goals for the future. Spiritual directors, pastors, and your religious community are another invaluable resource to help you maintain a balanced approach to wellness that enables you to use your personal talents to help the people around you. Longevity planning lays down the framework for the story that we want to write with this one life we've been given. Coaches help us to stay the course and help us troubleshoot along the way.

Set goals for yourself and continue to write your story day by day. But remember that you did not design yourself, and to fight against the will of the One who made you is a struggle that will only detract from your success and keep you from fulfilling your purpose. In Jeremiah 29:11, we are reminded that God has a plan for each human He has created, and we were each specifically designed to walk the path ahead of us. Wellness is a part of your plan, and each of us can benefit from the support and guidance of others.

“Listen to advice and accept discipline, and at the end, you will be counted among the wise. Many are the plans in a person’s heart, but it is the Lord’s purpose that prevails.”

Proverbs 19:20–21

Chapter 9
Misplacing Your Value

"God doesn't want something from us, He simply wants us."
– C. S. Lewis

In chapter ten, we are going to get into the actual assessments and techniques for achieving the condition of wellness that will support you on your journey and prepare you for all of the greatness that you were made for. But first, it is important to me to express to you the fundamental reason that you should pursue this wellness. You are valuable. Read that sentence as many times as you need to. You are valuable, and there isn't anything you can do to change that. Furthermore, there isn't anything you can do to become more valuable. You just are. You were as valuable from the moment of your conception as you will be at your last breath with a lifetime of accomplishments behind you. You are worthy of love and freedom and opportunity because you were created in the image and likeness of God. If you aren't sure that you share this belief with me, that's OK. Most people would at least agree that all human beings deserve life, liberty, and the pursuit of happiness, and whether you believe that it is given to you by God or the universe, we should all unite on this truth and seek to secure and maintain those rights for all people.

In the Bible, the apostle John is referred to as 'John the Beloved' or 'the one whom Jesus loved.' This never bothered me, but it did often strike me as a little strange. Didn't Jesus love everyone equally? It wasn't until just a few years ago when I realized that it is actually John who refers to *himself* as 'the one whom Jesus loved.' When I read this, it seemed even more strange. It sounded odd because it reads as though John is making a point to say that he was somehow Jesus's favorite. It didn't bother me enough to ever look into it, and so I've always just accepted that that was the way we referred to John. To be fair, he was the only apostle that was present at the crucifixion, so maybe he earned it!

Personally, over the last few years, I have experienced a lot of changes in my life and I was left questioning my own value. I found myself fighting the feeling of worthlessness on a regular basis. I don't believe this is a struggle unique to me, and that is why I feel that it is necessary to highlight the importance of recognizing our true value before we get into the nuts and bolts of wellness and purpose. Around this same time, I had begun going weekly to Eucharistic adoration which is an hour before the Blessed Sacrament. Our parish is lucky enough to have a chapel open 24 hours a day, and I had the chance to spend one hour a week alone in the chapel talking to Jesus. I quoted St. Theresa of Calcutta earlier in the book, and it is worth mentioning again, never has it been so clear to me that prayer does not necessarily change things, but it does 'change us and we change things.' It is amazing what one hour a week can do for your mind, body, and spirit health. Being the long-winded list maker that I am, I would find it difficult to cram in all of the items on my agenda at my weekly adoration hour. If I managed to check all of them off of my list, I usually felt accomplished and inspired. If my mind wandered or I couldn't think of what I wanted to say, I would leave wondering if I had just wasted precious time.

Not long after signing up for my weekly hour, I began thinking about what it was that I had to offer and what I should be doing with my life. As I mentioned, I didn't feel especially passionate about my job even though I loved working with my patients. I wasn't sure where I should be volunteering or helping out, and I was always wondering whether I was doing the right thing for my kids. I had heard a great homily by Father Jason Worley about how God gives each of us gifts, and all He asks is that we offer them back to Him through worship and service to others. The homily was a meditation on how ancient people would offer burnt sacrifices. The gesture and prayers were all about offering the first fruits back to God in thanksgiving and in petition for more blessings. These days, we do not offer burnt sacrifices any longer, and if you are of a Christian faith, this is because Jesus has already come as the ultimate sacrifice to end all sacrifices, and His death was a perfect offering to atone for the sins of mankind. This does not mean, however, that we are not called to continue to sacrifice or offer the best of ourselves to God.

Father Jason spoke about how God turns any willing offering into something even greater and that this is how we serve others to the best of our ability. Money is the obvious offering that comes to mind, and while it is, of course, important to offer our financial support to charities, there are many, many more gifts that we are asked to share with the world. So, I began meditating on what it was that I had to offer. I didn't have much money and I didn't have a lot of time. I didn't feel that I had any wisdom that would make any major impact or any real talents to share. This made me begin to seriously question my value. What I lacked in resources and ability, I vowed to make up for in volume. I decided I would just start to do 'more.' I took on more work and sought to be as busy as possible. This was as unfulfilling as you might expect.

One night at adoration, I found myself anxious over how much I had to do and was running through a list of what I had recently accomplished. Very clearly, I experienced a moment of deep simplicity (which is the best way I can describe a thought that I don't believe came from my own brain) and I heard in my head the words: "You are valuable because I say so." Like most of you, I had tied my value to something other than my truest identity. For as long as I can remember, I have measured my value based on what I have produced. The more I do, the more valuable I feel. I had made independence more important than anything else. But none of us were designed to be fully self-sufficient, and that sentiment is rooted only in pride. My relationships had suffered, my finances had suffered, and my health had suffered. Overcome in the moment, the words of St. John the Beloved were so clear to me, he refers to himself as the 'one whom Jesus loved' because that is the single most important part of his identity. He is acknowledging that it does not matter if he has any particular talent, pedigree, or wealth, but that he is valuable only because he is loved by the One who died in order to demonstrate how valuable we all are. "The one whom Jesus loved" IS John's identity, and it's your truest identity too. It is a reality that I must repeat to myself every single day, and I hope you will as well. We live in a world dominated by our five senses and we seek validation in whatever areas of our life mean the most. Some people feel valuable when others validate their beauty or sex appeal, others feel valuable if they have wealth or power. We measure success by how we are doing compared to others and by whether or not other people believe that we are important. But the simple reality is you are valuable, no matter your shortcomings or disabilities, simply because God says you are.

Again, if you don't share this belief, stick with me. I believe you are valuable and I want you to be well too. Rarely do we invest true time and effort into things that we do not believe are worthy. If you do not believe that you are worthy of wellness, you will have great difficulty in loving yourself enough to commit to healthy habits and practices. But don't be discouraged. Everyone gets down on themselves from time to time, and your core wellness tribe and coaches should be there to help you remember your value.

Once we have at least acknowledged that we are valuable and have committed ourselves to continuing to understand and grow in that truth, we must then set out to put our value to great use. CS Lewis reflects on another author's metaphor about God's will for our lives by saying, "God is easy to please but hard to satisfy." The author was writing about a father being happy to see his toddler take his first few steps. The father is proud and joyful watching his little one learn to walk. But, of course, the toddler's father also expects that when his son grows up, he will walk tall and strong like a grown man. God absolutely accepts us for who we are and takes joy in watching us set out in pursuit of a holistically healthy life, but He expects us to continue to grow in faith and to do great things by using the gifts that he provides to us. CS Lewis went on to write one of the most convicting reflections from the perspective of Jesus that I have ever read:

> "Make no mistake," He says, "if you let me, I will make you perfect. The moment you put yourself in My hands, that is what you are in for. Nothing less, or other, than that. You have free will, and if you choose, you can push Me away. But if you do not push Me away, understand that I am going to see this job through. Whatever suffering it may cost you in your earthly life, whatever inconceivable purification it may cost you after death, whatever it costs Me, I will never rest, nor let you rest, until you are literally perfect—until my Father can say without reservation that He is well pleased with you, as He said He was well pleased with me. This I can do and will do. But I will not do anything less."

This is both intimidating and wonderfully inspiring. And if you are a parent, you have experienced some level of this love and motivation in your own life. My children are valuable to me simply 'because.' There is nothing that would make me love them less, and they are no more or less valuable to me today than when I first saw their tiny heartbeats pounding away on the sonogram screen. In the gospel according to John, Jesus says, "I give you a new commandment—to love one another. Just as I have loved you, you are also to love one another." (John 13:34) This again speaks to our value and gives us the standard by which we are to love others. If God loves us, not for what we can produce or what we look like or for how useful we are but simply 'because,' then that is how we are to value and love others.

Think about the relationships in your life and the people you 'love.' Do you love them for what they give you? Do you love them because of how they make you feel or how they make you look? Do you love them only when they are doing what you want them to do? If so, you may not really love them at all. You were designed to be love, but just as Jesus sets the example of the Master becoming the servant, we must also be ever mindful that we were first designed to love God above all things, and to love our neighbors as we love ourselves. God does demand greatness of us, and it is good to set the bar high for ourselves and for others. Not to set ourselves up for failure, but to support one another in making the best choices we can and fulfilling our purpose to the best of our ability.

One of my favorite saints, and my youngest daughter's namesake, is St. Catherine of Siena. She famously says, "Be what God meant you to be and you will set the world on fire." Because I love my children, I don't want them to live a mediocre life that will leave them with deathbed regret, and God doesn't want that for them either. Because your value has been established by God, you should be encouraged to strive to achieve true wellness in order to fulfill the mission He has set before you. If we choose to acknowledge how we were designed, what we were designed for, and who designed us, we can seize the opportunity to truly live life to the fullest. This is where it all comes together, by choosing here and now to write the rest of your story with better knowledge, more support, and positive intention, you can avoid your deathbed regrets and experience what it feels like to be the best version of yourself.

Before we begin, let me share with you the final straw that led me to all of this. At the beginning of the book, I wrote about how all of this started for me. In 2011, I was finally able to articulate what I wanted to do, thanks to a personal experience that left me wanting to pursue better holistic wellness for myself, and to find a way to elevate health coaching to the next level for the people that I serve. I gave birth to my third beautiful baby in 2011. I nursed her, just like the other two, only, at this point in my life, things were a little bit different.

I had two other young children at home, we had moved several times and there were new financial challenges. My oldest started kindergarten, my job and schedule were more challenging, and like many families with young kids, it seemed like someone was always sick! My children weren't great sleepers, I felt pressure to lose baby weight, and I was cooking mostly for a five-year-old and a toddler. I began developing severe mouth ulcers. Before having children, I would occasionally get them, especially when I got sick, and I had experienced them more severely when I was nursing my first two children, but absolutely nothing like this third time around. They bled, they were very painful, and it was hard to speak or eat. They got worse at night, and I remember trying hard to ignore the pain so I could read bedtime stories to the kids. During this time, I always had at least one, but sometimes I had as many as six at once. I called my doctor for an appointment and was told that there wasn't anything that could be done about a canker sore so that as long as I didn't have a fever, there was no point in coming in for an appointment. Around this same time, I was getting very dizzy when I stood up quickly, especially at night. I was seeing spots almost all of the time, and my hands would go numb often and for no reason. All of these symptoms were wearing on me.

I started to panic that I had a serious condition, and the panic lead to persistent anxiety. My panic attacks had already become a great burden after I had given birth to my third child, just before the sores and other symptoms began. I never experienced postpartum depression the way I had heard it described and didn't realize that the severe spike in my panic attacks was a similar and common condition. This went on for months. On better days, I just accepted that my symptoms were 'normal,' and that pain, fatigue, dizziness, and anxiety were just a part of life. On worse days, I would panic that I had an undiagnosed disease and would obsessively worry about my future. Spiritually, I tried to persist in my prayers and devotions but felt very isolated and frustrated that my prayers seemed to go unanswered.

Slowly but surely, I began to piece things together and became convinced that I had some sort of deficiency due to multiple pregnancies and years of nursing my babies. I made another appointment with my doctor. When I arrived, I explained my symptoms with particular emphasis on the painful sores. He spent about 3 minutes in the exam room with me. He didn't ask me one question about my sleep habits or my diet. After listening to my chest and looking at my throat, he scribbled a script and handed it to me. The prescription was for a medication to treat a specific virus. Confused, I asked him if he believed I had this virus, to which he replied, "No, you don't, but I don't know what else to give you, so maybe that'll help. There's nothing else you can do, you're a tired mom like the rest of them." I never even had the prescription filled. But a new resolve came over me that day to figure out how to make myself better.

I was becoming more confident and more convinced that I was designed to be well and someone out there could help me figure it out. A few weeks later, I had done enough research to figure out that I had a simple B12 deficiency. B12 is found in poultry, beef, eggs, milk, and fish. As a mother of young, picky eaters, we rarely made fish or beef, and I only ate a small portion or so of chicken each week. I don't like milk, and because I don't like eggs cooked the same way my children did, I often prepared eggs only for them. Once I figured it out, I didn't even bother to purchase a supplement, I simply made a conscious effort to add B12 foods to my diet.

In a matter of only a few weeks, the sores were gone, the dizziness and numbness subsided, and I wasn't seeing spots. The relief in my physical symptoms also led to a gradual decrease in the anxiety that I was struggling to cope with. I was sleeping better and waking up feeling rested—even with a poorly sleeping baby! This was the beginning of it all for me. If adding a few simple foods to my diet had such a huge effect, what else could I do? I experimented with fasting, cleanses to remove sugar and gluten, and made an effort to eat more quality produce. I broadened my fitness pursuits to be more holistic by incorporating cross training and began exploring more meaningful career options. I started going to Eucharistic adoration, as I mentioned, and asked friends for spiritual book recommendations. This was, of course, just the beginning of my new approach to wellness, and I am still troubleshooting my way through parts of it, but along the way, I found myself called to share this wellness with others. And so here I am. In the next chapter, we are going to put it into practice, and I can't wait for you to start feeling great. Because I know how valuable you are.

Chapter 10
Achieving Wellness
Practical Body, Mind, and Spirit Wellness Techniques

"I was born to do this."
– St. Joan of Arc

Earlier in the book, I asked you to consider ten questions that would help you to begin contemplating a change and shared my four goals for making the jump from contemplation to action. Now we move to real action items. I saved the discussion of value until the end of the book because I hope that the awareness of each component of self, the role of epigenetics, and the effects of imbalance have given you a better perspective on what challenges and threatens your wellness and why you should believe in the possibility of becoming holistically healthy. . Without self-awareness and objective health measures, it can be difficult to have a true sense of value. Each of us has the opportunity to start pursuing wellness today. It does not matter how old you are, what illnesses you have suffered from, or how long you have allowed bad habits to dictate your behavior, leave the past behind because you were definitely born to do this.

So here are the Ten Core Beliefs for Professional Health Coaching:

1. You have a body designed to carry you through life and heal from illnesses and injuries.
2. You have a mind designed to experience, remember, and learn each and every day. Your mind processes the information sensed by the body and makes decisions based on the needs of the body and morality of the soul.
3. You have a soul that transcends this life and seeks communion with God. Your soul pursues truth and has a dynamic relationship with body and mind.
4. Having a coach or coaches to help you navigate body, mind, and spirit wellness is not only a good idea, but necessary. We all need help.
5. Desiring wellness is not selfish, but it can become a vain pursuit unless you use your holistic health to serve the people around you.
6. Perfect balance is neither possible nor essential, but an awareness of imbalance and a plan to course-correct when necessary are crucial to achieving holistic health.
7. Living in the past, clinging to bad habits, and accepting dysfunction as 'normal' will leave you with deathbed regret and a life story that you did not want to write. The professional health coaching principle of Root Cause Reversal incorporates the assessments necessary to discover the conditions that make wellness difficult for you in order to provide you with a great level of self-awareness.

8. Living only in the now via instant gratification and/or avoidance will continue to perpetuate the mistakes and conditions of the past. The only way to break free from that which makes you ill or prevents you from living the life you were meant to live is to practice self-control through obedience and to humble yourself enough to ask for help. The professional health coaching principle of Active Symptom Treatment principle addresses the primary manifestation of your biggest challenges so you can overcome them.
9. Living in the future, whether optimistic but uncommitted or optimistic but controlling, is no way to ensure that you will find purpose or fulfillment. Likewise, living in the future full of angry or despairing pessimism will drain you of your resolve and isolate you from those who can help. The Longevity Planning principle is not only helpful but essential in piecing together a strategy that supports your goals and guides you in living as well as you can for yourself and those around you.
10. Your value has nothing to do with what you produce or what you have to offer. Your value is innate and due to the fact that you were designed in the image and likeness of God. Furthermore, you are called to acknowledge the value of others according to their design. Whether you feel optimistic or pessimistic about the future at any moment in time is beside the point, true wellness should be built on the desire to become an

Intentional Servant who leaves the world better for having been in it.

So Where Do I Start?

Traditional health coaching acknowledges the process by which someone goes from a pre-contemplative perspective on wellness all the way through planning, action, and maintenance. But the approach to this process varies based on your current level of health. Effective professional health coaching must be able to serve all people in all settings and provide specialized programming and support to help you meet your goals. After years of providing therapy to clients with all types of illnesses and injuries, of all ages, and in all settings, I have separated my approach into three categories: Prevention, Transition, and High-Risk Relapse.

Prevention is the most basic level of professional health coaching and one that seeks to serve anyone who has not suffered a major illness or injury. Those who have suffered a major illness or injury but have fully recovered are also appropriate for this level of intervention. While most of us agree that prevention is wise, acting on that wisdom can sometimes be a challenge. When we feel generally well and are able to go about our daily lives without too much pain or difficulty, it can be tempting to put better habits off until tomorrow. For the Prevention level of coaching, the pillars are most effective when prioritized in the following order: Longevity Planning, Root Cause Reversal, Active Symptom Treatment. Longevity Planning is a more comprehensive perspective on the future than financial and retirement planning alone. Longevity Planning not only incorporates a proactive approach to health concerns, but also asks that important deathbed question.

For those of us in the Prevention category for health coaching intervention, it is most helpful to zoom out of our current circumstances and try to see the big picture. If I lived a long life, how many decades could I have left? When do I plan to or need to retire? How much older or younger is my spouse? How many children do I have or hope to have, and am I likely to live near them? Will my parents and/or in-laws need me to be around to help take care of them? What health concerns am I already beginning to face, and what am I most worried about having to deal with? There are many more questions to consider, but you get the idea! As you piece together these answers, you will have a few answers that you are very certain of, many that you are relatively certain of, and a few that are simply educated guesses.

Once you have a basic idea of what your future may look like, you can start to see your life as it is currently being written and compare that against the story that you hope to have written when it is all said and done. This does not mean that you can choose each and every detail of your life, but it is within your power to identify areas of your life that are leading you places you do not want to go and to seek out the help and resources you need to make better choices. Remembering that we were designed to be well and considering the environmental challenges that we face in our current day and age, a health coach is an excellent resource in determining which medical issues may be waiting for you in your future unless you incorporate healthier habits here and now. As I mentioned before, we live in an especially exciting age of medicine and are now able to see more clearly the relationship between our environmental exposure and our internal function. With or without actual lab testing, a qualified professional health coach should be able to evaluate your current condition as well as your predisposition to various diseases and make specific recommendations to optimize your mind and body function.

The Root Cause Reversal pillar is the second priority for the prevention level of coaching and gets to the heart of wellness issues and develops a personalized plan that can treat today's symptoms, prevent tomorrow's diseases, and actually reverse damage that has already been done. Your miraculous body was designed to heal itself, and understanding the cause of your issues is the number one way to achieve the health you are working towards.

The final pillar for the prevention group is Active Symptom Treatment. So often, those of us who are not dealing with serious illness, acute injuries, or other scary health scenarios go about our days ignoring health issues that impact our mind and body function. Some of us complain, some of us don't, but most of us just carry on without seeking any real help. Fatigue, pain, irritability, insomnia, and a whole host of other symptoms are just 'part of life' as we know it, and we accept that it must just be a normal part of aging. While Longevity Planning and Root Cause Reversal seek to shine a light on these symptoms and address their cause and impact on the future, Active Symptom Treatment meets them head on and helps the body speed up the healing process. Active Symptom Treatment uses all sorts of modalities; functional movement interventions, massage therapy, oils, natural remedies, stress reduction techniques, myofascial release, bracing or splinting, and counseling, among many others, are methods to address your most worrisome or bothersome symptoms before they become something more significant.

Transition is the next level of professional health coaching. The needs of this group are the primary reason that I began researching new ways to serve my patients. People who fall into this category have recently experienced an illness or injury and have already received the necessary treatment for stabilization. For many, these episodes require a hospitalization or maybe even inpatient rehabilitation. These episodes can occur at any age and for a wide variety of reasons. As a therapist, I treated patients in hospitals, subacute rehab settings, and in their homes once they had been discharged. Home health care was a great setting to work in because it gave me the opportunity to help people in their own personal environment, often surrounded by their support network of friends and family.

During the initial evaluation, one of the most valuable pieces of information that I needed to collect was a solid picture of their life prior to their illness or injury. The objective of therapy is to help someone return to their prior level of function. Sometimes, this isn't possible, but more often, it is. While I do understand the necessary limits of the healthcare system, I often found myself frustrated at having to discharge a patient before I felt confident that they had achieved adequate wellness and were ready to maintain their progress alone. One of my coworkers felt the same way, and together, she and I began to develop programming to fill in the gaps between sickness and wellness.

A few years ago, I began following some of my patients informally once they had been required to discontinue therapy services. I would continue to provide training and support without insurance reimbursement so I could maximize my patient's potential and help to ensure a successful transition back to their homes and jobs. After seeing the value and success in this practice, the need to develop formal Transition programming was evident.

In order for people who fall into the Transition category to not only recover from illness or injury, but to use the momentum of their recovery to fuel a commitment to wellness, the pillars of professional health coaching can be reordered into effective programming. It is even more important for this category to seek out highly qualified health coaches who have a strong background in rehabilitation in order to create a meaningful, personalized plan that considers their health conditions. Active Symptom Treatment is the best pillar to start with for the Transition group. This is because they have recently been receiving treatment for their condition and are likely being actively monitored by a doctor or medical team. Once a patient has been discharged from rehabilitative treatment, they are expected to maintain their progress and continue on in their wellness journey. This transition is necessary, though many people have difficulty with this stage in their recovery. Professional health coaching can continue to provide some of these useful treatment techniques or provide additional training that helps to turn good practice into meaningful lifestyle changes.

In my opinion, nutrition and functional movement are the most useful components to Active Symptom Treatment.

While both of these are addressed to some degree during a recovery from illness or injury, post-rehabilitation is the ideal time to focus on realistic goals in these areas. Root Cause Reversal is the next pillar for someone in Transition. Root Cause Reversal is an excellent way to address the history of their present illness without interrupting current treatment strategies. By utilizing formal or informal genetic testing and identifying specific lifestyle changes to help support a full recovery, a health coach can become a useful member of a medical team that is already in place.

Longevity Planning is the final pillar for this group but no less crucial. While someone is coping with the extra burden of physical or mental illness, it is difficult to focus on the future. A health coach can help structure longevity planning into both short-term and long-term goals, making long-term health and wellness more accessible and achievable. Short-term longevity planning can focus on the next six month to a year. Creating a plan to survive physically and financially during a recovery from illness or injury can help to avoid catastrophic consequences that can send you further down Maslow's pyramid than is necessary. A health coach can provide you with the information and support you need to coordinate your wellness efforts with your family, work supervisors, and financial advisor.

The final level of professional health coaching is High-Risk Relapse. Three variations of high-risk relapse exist but all are approached in the same way. Some people who fall into this category have a condition which is both serious and difficult to treat, putting them at a higher risk for becoming symptomatic or needing increased services. Others in this category suffer from multiple conditions and are often treated by multiple medications, making it difficult to achieve balance.

The final cause for High-Risk Relapse is a lack of cooperation or compliance on the part of the patient or client. There is a common statistic used to describe those who fall into this category and multiple studies have upheld the staggering claim: about 80% of healthcare dollars are spent on just 20% of the population. To break the cycle of illness and achieve a lasting level of health and wellness, the people in this category need a supportive and collaborative team of coaches. Specialized programming to address the unique needs of this population will not only lead to better outcomes for patients, but will save money as well. When we consider the greater than average extra burden on these people, it is clear that in order to overcome the strain on each component of self, additional time and coaching are needed to adjust to necessary lifestyle changes. Too often, sickness leads to financial stress which then prevents a person from healing. The cycle of illness and stress continues with not enough resources for the healing individual to fully recover. This category is best served by addressing the pillars in the following order: Root Cause Reversal, Longevity Planning, and Active Symptom Treatment.

While someone in transition may be still actively recovering and, therefore, benefit from Active Symptom Treatment being the priority in coaching, someone who has recovered but is at a high risk for becoming ill again should take the opportunity to focus primarily on Root Cause Reversal. This is the ideal time to make sure that the running sink is turned off once and for all. By providing this population with advanced, personalized programming and support, the need for future interventions can be significantly decreased. Circumstances specific to each individual may dictate whether Longevity Planning or Active Symptom Treatment are the next priority for this level of health coaching, but when possible, I believe that Longevity Planning can be most impactful. Whether caused by severity or a lack of compliance, those who fall into the category of High-Risk Relapse can greatly benefit from the opportunity to refocus on the story they hope to one day tell and the goal of becoming Intentional Servants. Seizing the opportunity to set both short-term and long-term goals can help to break the cycle of sickness and stress. Continuing to address any symptoms that interfere with all components of self, in any capacity, through the Active Symptom Treatment pillar should be as specific as possible and ongoing when necessary.

Taking the Next Step

Most of us can probably identify which group we belong to, and once you know, you can get started.

1. Seek out your first coach. Finding a professional health coach is a great place to start. This should be someone who is certified, able to provide you with specialized assessments and planning, and is not trying to sell you something.
2. Begin building your tribe. Look for groups that you can belong to both virtually and in person to help keep you on course. Your tribe should definitely include opportunities for fitness but

should not be limited to physical activity. Religious organizations, support groups, and interest groups are important components to your tribe.

3. Complete a self-assessment. Take some time to sit down and consider each component of self. Write down the strengths and weaknesses as you see them for your body, mind, and spirit. Once you have made your list, step back to look at the big picture and consider what story you are on pace to tell versus the story you hope to tell.
4. Commit yourself to physical effort. You may be a soul but you do have a body, and it needs maintenance. Your health coach should guide you through a functional movement program, but be sure to engage in physical activity each day whether your coach is there or not.
5. Fast. Each of us was built to fast in one way or another. Begin today by eliminating one unhealthy or unnecessary thing from diet (without replacing it with something else!) and limit your hours of eating to a smaller window.
6. Share the mental burden. While some people may be able to achieve better mental health by organizing the above steps, others will need more intensive support. Seek out an additional coach through counseling or organized support group and do not isolate from those who can help you.
7. Begin to pray or meditate. If you are someone who is used to daily prayer, consider adding five minutes of silence to your day or adding a new

category of spiritual reading. If you are someone unfamiliar with spiritual practice, begin with a daily meditation book, scripture reading, or recitation of familiar prayers.

8. Take control of your surroundings. Before adding to your routine or environment, take the opportunity to clean and declutter. This includes your physical environment which can have a major impact on all components of self, as well as your routines, habits, and relationships that detract from your health rather than support it. Basic organization may be easy enough to accomplish on your own but be sure to seek the support of your coaches and tribes for more challenging tasks.

Nurturing the Spirit

Remember that this story that you are writing is going to take a lifetime—literally. You will not accomplish your goals all at once, and there will be setbacks. As a new mom, I heard a lot of conversation about finding balance and maintaining routine. I discovered that my own definition of routine and the criteria that I helped my patients to follow was less about perfection and more about intention. Things will never go exactly as planned all of the time, even for the Aggressive Optimist, but that does not mean that you should abandon structure. Balance and routine are about creating a foundation to return to. Whether through an unbalanced pursuit or an extra burden, you will often find yourself off course and struggling to regain balance. The routine you create with the support of your coaches and tribe is the foundation that you should seek to return to when you experience imbalance. At the heart of this routine should be that which nurtures your spirit. If your physical and mental goals do not elevate your spiritual wellness, they will not support lasting, holistic health. At the heart of all of your efforts should be an intention to seek truth and fulfill purpose rather than achieving some measure of perfection. Each day traveling in this great big ship, we should get closer to the One who designed us.

Putting Your Wellness into Action

As we discussed in chapter 8, our outlook on the future is not necessarily the best guide for our actions. To be frank, whether you are a natural born optimist or pessimist doesn't need to matter. Following your heart may sound poetic but it is not best practice. Feelings come and go, and so instead, it is our intentions that we should commit ourselves to fulfilling. Becoming the Intentional Servant you were designed to be will not only make good use of your wellness but will help you to maintain it. These are the four considerations of the Intentional Servant as I see them:

1. Respect. Each of us should acknowledge the value of one another. How do you demonstrate your respect for others on a daily basis? How do you demonstrate respect for those who are often overlooked and forgotten?
2. Protect. There are so many vulnerable populations throughout the world who are at a grave disadvantage in many ways and cannot always

protect themselves. Do you use your abilities and influence to protect those who need help?

3. Forgive. This is often much easier said than done, but that doesn't change the fact that it is necessary. Forgive, no matter what, and you will be much healthier.
4. Serve. Your wellness is meaningless unless it does good in the world. Regardless of what level of wellness you have achieved so far, there is something that you can do each day to serve someone else.

How Can I Help My Loved Ones?

Once you have committed yourself to making some healthy changes and begin feeling the effects of a better lifestyle, you will likely want to share your newfound wellness with your friends and family. This is part of building your core wellness tribe and will help you to maintain your own progress. In addition to the motivated participants in your life, however, you may have some family members who are either unwilling or unable to create and stick to a wellness plan. Family dynamics, multiple generations, and conflicting interests can make it difficult to implement family-wide changes, and the frustration and wasted effort can derail your own personal progress. This is not at all limited to one component of self. Whether convincing your family to give up sweets, communicate with more respect, or begin going to church regularly, you are likely to experience both mutual successes and frustrating failures. Over the years, I have had the opportunity to get up close and personal with hundreds of families in the privacy of their own homes as they navigate through many of these challenges. Here are some things to consider when helping your loved ones achieve the wellness they were designed to enjoy:

1. You cannot be all things to all people. Your loved ones need a tribe and coaches of their own, and while you may be the most influential person in their life or responsible for the majority of their care, you cannot do it all. Your children, parents, siblings, and even spouse need other people in their life to fill certain roles. I have watched many relationships suffer badly when someone tries to become nurse, therapist, and counselor to their loved one. Inevitably, the most important role, that of family member, is compromised and sabotages attempts at wellness.
2. You cannot change everything all at once. This won't work for you and it definitely won't work for your family. By instituting sweeping changes to your household or lifestyle and setting grand, unrealistic expectations, you are most certainly setting yourself and your loved ones up for failure.
3. It is never too early. Your children cannot create their own environment, so whatever environment you create for yourself will be the one that they are influenced by. If you eat healthier, they will likely eat at least a little healthier too. If you are outside and exercising more often, they will be moving more often too. If you behave more calmly, they will soak up that peace and patience. If you make church a priority, they will grow up with that habit.

4. But remember, your kids have their own unique set of genes! If you suspect that your child is burdened with dysfunctional genes that require special attention, they have access to the same great epigenetic science that you do. Don't hesitate to empower your child with the tools to change their life for the better.
5. It is never too late. Your parents may be advanced in years and have lifelong habits to contend with, but their bodies are still inclined to heal themselves. As we age, healing and regeneration may take longer, but they are still possible. One of the most common misconceptions and attitudes that I run into when I work with patients is the belief that "it can't get any worse." It can and it will get worse without intervention. Healthy lifestyle changes can have a major impact on older adults and allow people to age in place, enjoy the winter of their lives, spend less money on medical intervention, and avoid unnecessary burden on their children and grandchildren. Consider giving them the gift of good health! Health coaching, wellness services, and genetic testing are great gifts to give to your parents, and you don't have to wait for a special occasion.
6. Include your spouse. While there may be some challenges to getting your spouse on board, you will go much farther together than you will on your own. Keep in mind that you are equal partners and you are not 'in charge' of your spouse's wellness. Though your tribes may vary a little, you will benefit from having a unified team of coaches to help guide your health, finances, and spirituality. Couples counseling isn't just for spouses in crisis. Being proactive about your relationship will

improve your holistic health. Encourage one another and enjoy each other's wellness!

You were definitely born to do this. You were designed, created, and born to live a life that matters and to leave a mark on the world. Whether you wake up tomorrow feeling optimistic or pessimistic about your future does not need to interfere with your story. Choose to be an Intentional Servant who helps others climb the pyramid by offering your time and talents to the people around you. Demonstrate gratitude for your wellness by using it to serve. When you feel burdened or discouraged, seek support from your tribe and remember that they need you too.

Epilogue: Pursuing Truth and Purpose with Your Wellness

"Pride sets subtle snares. Whenever we imagine that we are in control of life, our own or someone else's, we have fallen prey to the ancient whisper in the Garden: 'You shall be like gods.'"

I believe in the value of coaching and of belonging to groups of people who inspire your wellness because your relationships with others will give purpose to your life. Once you address any current illnesses or troubling symptoms of mind, body, or spirit and develop a solid longevity plan with your advisors, you will be ready to begin putting your good health to good use! Lifelong wellness will always require work and attention, but once you have committed yourself to a better lifestyle, you will be more able to experience and accomplish the things in your life that you choose to pursue. Throughout the book, I have mentioned the pursuit of truth and the desire to fulfill your own individual purpose. Yet again, I'll point out that I am not qualified to write a book on truth, and my objective is not to tell you what you should do with your life once you are healthy. However, as I continue to develop my own practice and study various areas of holistic health, I notice the general acceptance of relativism and individual truth within the world of integrative medicine and alternative therapies. This is neither good science nor sound philosophy. Science acknowledges objective truths, and philosophy seeks meaning in those truths. 'Speak your truth' is a bold and empowering statement and is a popular theme in areas of holistic health. I believe that this statement is often made with the good intent to encourage people to be honest about who they are, what they have experienced, and what they hope to achieve. I wholeheartedly support the use of 'speak your truth' to empower vulnerable people to speak up about injustice and abuse that they have endured. However, this sentiment has a dark side that needs to be acknowledged before you can use the condition of your wellness to write a great story with your life. 'Speak your truth' implies that somehow each of us can create our own reality. It implies that if you want something to be true, it can be true. I urge you to reject this empty principle. Simply put, if everything is true, then nothing is true. With the great gift of wellness, we should spend our lives *seeking* truth instead of trying to create it. This does not mean that you should believe what I believe or what anyone else tells you to believe, but it does mean that you should be careful not to create your own reality. This is relevant to health and wellness for four reasons:

1. You did not design yourself, and therefore, the pursuit of discovering your origin is worth considering.
2. Believing in any practice or principle that is not aligned with your design will ultimately undermine your health no matter how much you commit to it.
3. Holistic health requires spiritual consideration and is not limited to one component of self or one personal interest.
4. Science is a great gift to us and one that gives us a glimpse into the mind-blowing design of the Creator. Awe-inspiring order can be observed all throughout nature, the universe, and the human body. When we submit to this order and live according to our design, we experience better health and the opportunity to climb the pyramid to self-actualization. When we reject our design, we disrupt this order which leads to illnesses of mind, body, and spirit. You were designed to seek and to serve and to be well.

"I desire only to know the truth and to live as well as I can, and to the utmost of my power, I exhort all other men to do the same."

– Socrates